CAPTAIN MACKLIN

"Go, Royal!" he cried, "and—God bless you!"

CAPTAIN MACKLIN

HIS MEMOIRS

BY

RICHARD HARDING DAVIS

ILLUSTRATED BY

Walter Appleton Clark

CHARLES SCRIBNER'S SONS
NEW YORK :::::::::::::::::: 1905

To

MY MOTHER

ILLUSTRATIONS

CAPTAIN MACKLIN

HIS MEMOIRS

I

UNITED STATES MILITARY ACADEMY,
WEST POINT

IT may seem presumptuous that so young a
man as myself should propose to write his life
and memoirs, for, as a rule, one waits until he has
accomplished something in the world, or until he
has reached old age, before he ventures to tell of
the times in which he has lived, and of his part in
them. But the profession to which I belong,
which is that of a soldier, and which is the noblest
profession a man can follow, is a hazardous one,
and were I to delay until to-morrow to write down
what I have seen and done, these memoirs might
never be written, for, such being the fortune of
war, to-morrow might not come.

So I propose to tell now of the little I have accomplished in the first twenty-three years of my
life, and, from month to month, to add to these
memoirs in order that, should I be suddenly taken
off, my debit and credit pages may be found care-

fully written up to date and carried forward. On the other hand, should I live to be an old man, this record of my career will furnish me with material for a more complete autobiography, and will serve as a safeguard against a failing memory.

In writing a personal narrative I take it that the most important events to be chronicled in the life of a man are his choice of a wife and his choice of a profession. As I am unmarried, the chief event in my life is my choice of a profession, and as to that, as a matter of fact, I was given no choice, but from my earliest childhood was destined to be a soldier. My education and my daily environment each pointed to that career, and even if I had shown a remarkable aptitude for any other calling, which I did not, I doubt if I would have pursued it. I am confident that had my education been directed in an entirely different channel, I should have followed my destiny, and come out a soldier in the end. For by inheritance as well as by instinct I was foreordained to follow the fortunes of war, to delight in the clash of arms and the smoke of battle; and I expect that when I do hear the clash of arms and smell the smoke of battle, the last of the Macklins will prove himself worthy of his ancestors.

I call myself the last of the Macklins for the reason that last year, on my twenty-second birthday, I determined I should never marry. Women I respect and admire, several of them, especially two of the young ladies at Miss Butler's Academy I have deeply loved, but a soldier cannot devote himself both to a woman and to his country. As one of our young professors said, "The flag is a jealous mistress."

The one who, in my earliest childhood, arranged that I should follow the profession of arms, was my mother's father, and my only surviving grandparent. He was no less a personage than Major-General John M. Hamilton. I am not a writer; my sword, I fear and hope, will always be easier in my hand than my pen, but I wish for a brief moment I could hold it with such skill, that I might tell of my grandfather properly and gratefully, and describe him as the gentle and brave man he was. I know he was gentle, for though I never had a woman to care for me as a mother cares for a son, I never missed that care; and I know how brave he was, for that is part of the history of my country. During many years he was my only parent or friend or companion; he taught me my lessons by day and my prayers by night, and, when I passed through all the absurd ailments to which a child is heir, he sat beside my cot and lulled me to sleep, or told me stories of the war. There was a childlike and simple quality in his own nature, which made me reach out to him and confide in him as I would have done to one of my own age. Later, I scoffed at this virtue in him as something old-fashioned and credulous. That was when I had reached the age when I was older, I hope, than I shall ever be again. There is no such certainty of knowledge on all subjects as one holds at eighteen and at eighty, and at eighteen I found his care and solicitude irritating and irksome. With the intolerance of youth, I could not see the love that was back of his anxiety, and which should have softened it for me with a halo and made me considerate and grateful. Now I see it—I see it now that it is too late. But surely he understood, he knew how I looked up to him, how I loved him, and how I tried to copy him, and, because I could not, consoled myself inwardly by thinking that the reason I had failed was because his way was the wrong one, and that my way was the better. If he did not understand then, he understands now; I cannot bear to think he does not understand and forgive me.

Those were the best days of my life, the days I spent with him as a child in his own home on the Hudson. It stands at Dobbs Ferry, set in a grove of pines, with a garden about it, and a box hedge that shuts it from the road. The room I

best remember is the one that overlooks the
Hudson and the Palisades. From its windows
you can watch the great vessels passing up and
down the river, and the excursion steamers flying
many flags, and tiny pleasure-boats and great
barges. There is an open fireplace in this room,
and in a corner formed by the book-case, and
next to the wood-box, was my favorite seat. My
grandfather's place was in a great leather chair beside the centre-table, and I used to sit cross-
legged on a cushion at his feet, with my back
against his knees and my face to the open hearth.
I can still see the pages of " Charles O'Malley "
and " Midshipman Easy," as I read them by the
lifting light of that wood fire, and I can hear the
wind roaring down the chimney and among the
trees outside, and the steamers signalling to each
other as they pushed through the ice and fog to
the great city that lay below us. I can feel the
fire burning my face, and the cold shivers that
ran down my back, as my grandfather told me of
the Indians who had once hunted in the very
woods back of our house, and of those he had
fought with on the plains. With the imagination
of a child, I could hear, mingled with the shrieks
of the wind as it dashed the branches against the
roof, their hideous war-cries as they rushed to
some night attack, or the howling of the wolves

in the snow. When I think of myself as I was then I am very fond of that little boy who sat shivering with excitement, and staring with open eyes at the pictures he saw in the firelight, a little boy who had made no enemies, no failures, who had harmed no one, and who knew nothing of the world outside the walls that sheltered him, save the brave old soldier who was his law and his example, his friend in trouble, and his playmate.

I knew nothing then, and I know very little now, either of my father or my mother. Whenever I asked my grandfather concerning them he always answered vaguely that he would tell me some day, "when you are of age," but whether he meant when I was twenty-one or of an age when I was best fitted to hear the truth, I shall never know. But I guessed the truth from what he let fall, and from what I have since heard from others, although that is but little, for I could not ask strangers to tell me of my own people. For some reason, soon after they were married my mother and father separated and she brought me to live with her father, and he entered the Southern army.

I like to think that I can remember my mother, and it seems I must, for very dimly I recollect a young girl who used to sit by the window looking out at the passing vessels. There is a daguerreo-type of my mother, and it may be that my recollection of her is builded upon that portrait. She died soon after we came to live with my grandfather, when I was only three years old, but I am sure I remember her, for no other woman was ever in the house, and the figure of the young girl looking out across at the Palisades is very clear to me.

My father was an Irish officer and gentleman, who came to the States to better his fortunes. This was just before the war; and as soon as it began, although he lived in the North, in New York City, he joined the Southern army and was killed. I believe, from what little I have learned of him, that he was both wild and reckless, but the few who remember him all say that he had many noble qualities, and was much loved by men, and, I am afraid, by women. I do not know more than that, except the one story of him, which my grandfather often told me.

"Whatever a man may say of your father," he would tell me, " you need not believe; for they may not have understood him, and all that you need to remember, until when you are of age I shall tell you the whole truth, is how he died." It is a brief story. My father was occupying a trench which for some hours his company had

part of demands for more stories, or for repetitions of those I already knew by heart, did more than any other thing to inspire me with a desire for military glory. My grandfather had served through the Mexican War, in the Indian campaigns on the plains, and during the War of the Rebellion, and his memory recalled the most wonderful and exciting of adventures. He was singularly modest, which is a virtue I never could consider as a high one, for I find that the world takes you at your own valuation, and unless "the terrible trumpet of Fame" is sounded by yourself no one else will blow your trumpet for you. Of that you may be sure. But I can't recall ever having heard my grandfather relate to people of his own age any of the adventures which he told me, and once I even caught him recounting a personal experience which redounded greatly to his credit as having happened to "a man in his regiment." When with childish delight I at once accused him of this he was visibly annoyed, and blushed like a girl, and afterward corrected me for being so forward in the presence of my elders. His modesty went even to the length of his keeping hidden in his bedroom the three presentation swords which had been given him at different times for distinguished action on the field. One came from the men of his regiment, one from his

townspeople after his return from the City of
Mexico, and one from the people of the State of
New York; and nothing I could say would in-
duce him to bring them downstairs to our sitting-
room, where visitors might see them. Personally, I cannot understand what a presentation
sword is for except to show to your friends; for,
as a rule, they are very badly balanced and of no
use for fighting.

Had it not been for the colored prints of the
different battles in Mexico which hung in our
sitting-room, and some Indian war-bonnets and
bows and arrows, and a box of duelling-pistols,
no one would have supposed that our house belonged to one of the most distinguished generals
of his day. You may be sure I always pointed
these out to our visitors, and one of my chief
pleasures was to dress one of my school-mates in
the Indian war-bonnet, and then scalp him with a
carving-knife. The duelling-pistols were even a
greater delight to me. They were equipped with
rifle-barrels and hair-triggers, and were inlaid
richly with silver, and more than once had been
used on the field of honor. Whenever my grandfather went out for a walk, or to play whist at the
house of a neighbor, I would get down these pistols and fight duels with myself in front of the
looking-glass. With my left hand I would hold

the handkerchief above my head, and with the other clutch the pistol at my side, and then, at the word, and as the handkerchief fluttered to the floor, I would take careful aim and pull the trigger. Sometimes I died and made speeches before I expired, and sometimes I killed my adversary and stood smiling down at him.

My grandfather was a member of the Aztec Club, which was organized during the occupation of the City of Mexico by the American officers who had stormed the capital; and on the occasion of one of its annual meetings, which that year was held in Philadelphia, I was permitted to accompany him to that city. It was the longest journey from home I had ever taken, and each incident of it is still clearly fixed in my mind. The event of the reunion was a dinner given at the house of General Patterson, and on the morning before the dinner the members of the club were invited to assemble in the garden which surrounded his house. To this meeting my grandfather conducted me, and I found myself surrounded by the very men of whom he had so often spoken. I was very frightened, and I confess I was surprised and greatly disappointed also to find that they were old and gray-haired men, and not the young and dashing warriors he had described. General Patterson alone did not disappoint me, for even at that late day he wore a blue coat with brass buttons and a buff waistcoat and high black stock. He had a strong, fine profile and was smooth shaven. I remember I found him exactly my ideal of the Duke of Wellington; for though I was only then ten or twelve years of age, I had my own ideas about every soldier from Alexander and Von Moltke to our own Captain Custer.

It was in the garden behind the Patterson house that we met the General, and he alarmed me very much by pulling my shoulders back and asking me my age, and whether or not I expected to be as brave a soldier as my grandfather, to which latter question I said, "Yes, General," and then could have cried with mortification, for all of the great soldiers laughed at me. One of them turned, and said to the only one who was seated, "That is Hamilton's grandson." The man who was seated did not impress me very much. He was younger than the others. He wore a black suit and a black tie, and the three upper buttons of his waistcoat were unfastened. His beard was close-cropped, like a blacking-brush, and he was chewing on a cigar that had burned so far down that I remember wondering why it did not scorch his mustache. And then, as I stood staring up at him and he down at me, it came over me who he was, and I can recall even now how my heart seemed to jump, and I felt terribly frightened and as though I were going to cry. My grandfather bowed to the younger man in the courteous, old-fashioned manner he always observed, and said: "General, this is my grandchild, Captain Macklin's boy. When he grows up I want him to be able to say he has met you. I am going to send him to West Point."

The man in the chair nodded his head at my grandfather, and took his cigar from his mouth and said, "When he's ready to enter, remind me, let me know," and closed his lips again on his cigar, as though he had missed it even during that short space of time. But had he made a long oration neither my grandfather nor I could have been more deeply moved. My grandfather said: "Thank you, General. It is very kind of you," and led me away smiling so proudly that it was beautiful to see him. When he had entered the house he stopped, and bending over me, asked, "Do you know who that was, Roy?" But with the awe of the moment still heavy upon me I could only nod and gasp at him.

"That was General Grant," my grandfather said.

"Yes, I know," I whispered.

I am not particularly proud of the years that

preceded my entrance to West Point, and of the years I have spent here I have still less reason to be content. I was an active boy, and behaved as other young cubs of that age, no better and no worse. Dobbs Ferry was not a place where temptations beset one, and, though we were near New York, we were not of it, and we seldom visited it. When we did, it was to go to a matinée at some theatre, returning the same afternoon in time for supper. My grandfather was very fond of the drama, and had been acquainted since he was a young man with some of the most distinguished actors. With him I saw Edwin Booth in " Macbeth," and Lester Wallack in " Rosedale," and John McCullough in " Virginius," a tragedy which was to me so real and moving that I wept all the way home in the train. Sometimes I was allowed to visit the theatre alone, and on these afternoons I selected performances of a lighter variety, such as that given by Harrigan & Hart in their theatre on Broadway. Every Thanksgiving Day I was allowed, after witnessing the annual football match between the students from Princeton and Yale universities, to remain in town all that night. On these great occasions I used to visit Koster & Bial's on Twenty-third Street, a long, low building, very dark and very smoky, and which on those nights was blocked with excited mobs of students, wearing different colored ribbons and shouting the cries of their different colleges. I envied and admired these young gentlemen, and thought them very fine fellows indeed. They wore in those days long green coats, which made them look like coachmen, and high, bell-shaped hats, both of which, as I now can see, were a queer survival of the fashions of 1830, and which now for the second time have disappeared.

To me, with my country clothes and manners and scanty spending money, the way these young collegians wagered their money at the football match and drank from their silver flasks, and smoked and swaggered in the hotel corridors, was something to be admired and copied. And although I knew none of them, and would have been ashamed had they seen me in company with any of my boy friends from Dobbs Ferry, I followed them from one hotel to another, pretending I was with them, and even penetrated at their heels into the café of Delmonico. I felt then for a brief moment that I was "seeing life," the life of a great metropolis, and in company with the young swells who made it the rushing, delightful whirlpool it appeared to be.

It seemed to me, then, that to wear a green coachman's coat, to rush the doorkeeper at the

Haymarket dance-hall, and to eat supper at the " Silver Grill " was to be " a man about town," and each year I returned to our fireside at Dobbs Ferry with some discontent. The excursions made me look restlessly forward to the day when I would return from my Western post, a dashing young cavalry officer on leave, and would wake up the cafés and clubs of New York, and throw my money about as carelessly as these older boys were doing then.

My appointment to West Point did not, after all, come from General Grant, but from President Arthur, who was in office when I reached my nineteenth year. Had I depended upon my Congressman for the appointment, and had it been made after a competitive examination of candidates, I doubt if I would have been chosen.

Perhaps my grandfather feared this and had it in his mind when he asked the President to appoint me. It was the first favor he had ever asked of the Government he had served so well, and I felt more grateful to him for having asked the favor, knowing what it cost him to do so, than I did to the President for granting it.

I was accordingly entered upon the rolls of the Military Academy, and my career as a soldier began. I wish I could say it began brilliantly, but the records of the Academy would not bear me out. Had it not been that I was forced to study books I would not have been a bad student; for in everything but books, in everything that bore directly on the training of a soldier and which depended upon myself, as, for example, drill, riding, marksmanship, and a knowledge of the manual, I did as well, or far better, than any of my classmates. But I could not, or would not, study, and instead of passing high in my class at the end of the plebe year, as my natural talents seemed to promise I would do, I barely scraped through, and the outlook for the second year was not encouraging. The campaign in Mexico had given my grandfather a knowledge of Spanish, and as a boy he had drilled this language into me, for it was a fixed belief of his, that if the United States ever went to war, it would be with some of her Spanish-American neighbors, with Mexico, or Central America, or with Spain on account of Cuba. In consequence he considered it most essential that every United States officer should speak Spanish. He also argued that a knowledge of French was of even greater importance to an officer and a gentleman, as it was, as I have since found it to be, the most widely spoken of all languages. I was accordingly well drilled in these two tongues, and I have never regretted the time I spent on them, for my facility in them has often served me well, has pulled me out of tight places, put money into my pocket, and gained me friends when but for them I might have remained and departed a stranger among strangers. My French accordingly helped me much as a "yearling," and in camp I threw myself so earnestly into the skirmish, artillery, and cavalry drills that in spite of my low marks I still stood high in the opinion of the cadet officers and of my instructors. With my classmates, for some reason, although in all out-of-door exercises I was the superior of most of them, I was not popular. I would not see this at first, for I try to keep on friendly terms with those around me, and I want to be liked even by people of whom I have no very high opinion and from whom I do not want anything besides. But I was not popular. There was no disguising that, and in the gymnasium or the riding-hall other men would win applause for performing a feat of horsemanship or a difficult trick on the parallel bars, which same feat, when I repeated it immediately after them, and even a little better than they had done it, would be received in silence. I could not see the reason for this, and the fact itself hurt me much more than anyone guessed. Then as they would not signify by their approbation that I was the best athlete in the class, I took to telling them that I was, which did not help matters. I find it is the same in the world as it is at the Academy—that if one wants recognition, he must pretend not to see that he deserves it. If he shows he does see it, everyone else will grow blind, holding, I suppose, that a conceited man carries his own comfort with him, and is his own reward. I soon saw that the cadet who was modest received more praise than the cadet who was his superior, but who, through repeated success, had acquired a self-confident, or, as some people call it, a conceited manner; and so, for a time, I pretended to be modest, too, and I never spoke of my athletic successes. But I was never very good at pretending, and soon gave it up. Then I grew morbid over my inability to make friends, and moped by myself, having as little to do with my classmates as possible. In my loneliness I began to think that I was a much misunderstood individual. My solitary state bred in me a most unhealthy disgust for myself, and, as it always is with those who are at times exuberantly light-hearted and self-assertive, I had terrible fits of depression and lack of self-confidence, during which spells I hated myself and all of those about me. Once, during one of these moods, a First-Class man, who had been a sneak in his plebe year and a bully ever since, asked me, sneeringly, how "Napoleon on the Isle of St. Helena " was feeling that morning, and I told him promptly to go to the devil, and added that if he addressed me again, except in the line of his duty, I would thrash him until he could not stand or see. Of course he sent me his second, and one of my classmates acted for me. We went out that same evening after supper behind Fort Clinton, and I thrashed him so badly that he was laid up in the hospital for several days. After that I took a much more cheerful view of life, and as it seemed hardly fair to make one cadet bear the whole brunt of my displeasure toward the entire battalion, I began picking quarrels with anyone who made pretensions of being a fighter, and who chanced to be bigger than myself.

Sometimes I got badly beaten, and sometimes I thrashed the other man, but whichever way it went, those battles in the soft twilight evenings behind the grass-grown ramparts of the old fort, in the shadow of the Kosciusko Monument, will always be the brightest and pleasantest memories of my life at this place.

My grandfather had one other daughter besides my mother, my Aunt Mary, who had married a Harvard professor, Dr. Endicott, and who had lived in Cambridge ever since they married.

Captain Macklin

In my second year here, Dr. Endicott died and my grandfather at once went to Cambridge to bring Aunt Mary and her daughter Beatrice back with him, installing them in our little home, which thereafter was to be theirs as well. He wrote me saying he knew I would not disapprove of this invasion of my place by my young cousin and assured me that no one, girl or boy, could ever take the place in his heart that I had held. As a matter of fact I was secretly pleased to hear of this addition to our little household. I knew that as soon as I was graduated I would be sent to some army post in the West, and that the occasional visit I was now able to pay to Dobbs Ferry would be discontinued. I hated to think that in his old age my grandfather would be quite alone. On the other hand, when, after the arrival of my cousin, I received his first letter and found it filled with enthusiastic descriptions of her, and of how anxious she was to make him happy, I felt a little thrill of jealousy. It gave me some sharp pangs of remorse, and I asked myself searchingly if I had always done my utmost to please my grandfather and to give him pride and pleasure in me. I determined for the future I would think only of how to make him happy.

A few weeks later I was able to obtain a few

hours' leave, and I wasted no time in running down from the Point to make the acquaintance of my cousin, and to see how the home looked under the new régime. I found it changed, and, except that I felt then and afterward that I was a guest, it was changed for the better.

I found that my grandfather was much more comfortable in every way. The newcomers were both eager and loving, although no one could help but love my grandfather, and they invented wants he had never felt before, and satisfied them, while at the same time they did not interfere with the life he had formerly led. Aunt Mary is an unselfish soul, and most content when she is by herself engaged in the affairs of the house and in doing something for those who live in it. Besides her unselfishness, which is to me the highest as it is the rarest of virtues, hers is a sweet and noble character, and she is one of the gentlest souls that I have ever known.

I may say the same of my cousin Beatrice. When she came into the room, my first thought was how like she was to a statuette of a Dresden shepherdess which had always stood at one end of our mantel-piece, coquetting with the shepherd lad on the other side of the clock. As a boy, the shepherdess had been my ideal of feminine loveliness. Since then my ideals had changed rapidly and often, but Beatrice reminded me that the shepherdess had once been my ideal. She wore a broad straw hat, with artificial roses which made it hang down on one side, and, as she had been working in our garden, she wore huge gloves and carried a trowel in one hand. As she entered, my grandfather rose hastily from his chair and presented us with impressive courtesy. "Royal," he said, "this is your cousin, Beatrice Endicott." If he had not been present, I think we would have shaken hands without restraint. But he made our meeting something of a ceremony. I brought my heels together and bowed as I have been taught to do at the Academy, and seeing this she made a low courtesy. She did this apparently with great gravity, but as she kept her eyes on mine I saw that she was mocking me. If I am afraid of anything it has certainly never proved to be a girl, but I confess I was strangely embarrassed. My cousin seemed somehow different from any of the other girls I had met. She was not at all like those with whom I had danced at the hotel hops, and to whom I gave my brass buttons in Flirtation Walk. She was more fine, more illusive, and yet most fascinating, with a quaint old-fashioned manner that at times made her seem quite a child, and the next moment changed her into a worldly and charming

He made our meeting something of a ceremony.

girl first informed me she thought a man who told her she was pretty was impertinent. What bewildered me still more on that occasion was that this particular girl was so extremely beautiful that to talk about anything else but her beauty was a waste of time. It made all other topics trivial, and yet she seemed quite sincere in what she said, and refused to allow me to bring our talk to the personal basis of "what I am to you" and "what you are to me." It was in discussing that question that I considered myself an artist and a master. My classmates agreed with me in thinking as I did, and from the first moment I came here called me "Masher" Macklin, a sobriquet of which I fear for a time I was rather proud. Certainly, I strove to live up to it. I believe I dignified my conduct to myself by calling it "flirtation." Flirtation, as I understood it, was a sort of game in which I honestly believed the entire world of men and women, of every class and age, were eagerly engaged. Indeed, I would have thought it rather ungallant, and conduct unworthy of an officer and a gentleman, had I not at once pretended to hold an ardent interest in every girl I met. This seems strange now, but from the age of fourteen up to the age of twenty that was my way of regarding the girls I met, and even to-day I fear my attitude toward them has altered but slightly, for now, although I no longer pretend to care when I do not, nor make love as a matter of course, I find it is the easiest attitude to assume toward most women. It is the simplest to slip into, just as I have certainly found it the one from which it is most difficult to escape. But I never seem to remember that until it is too late. A classmate of mine once said to me: "Royal, you remind me of a man walking along a road with garden gates opening on each side of it. Instead of keeping to the road, you stop at every gate, and say: 'Oh! what a pretty garden! I'll just slip in there, and find out where that path will take me.' And then—you're either thrown out, and the gate slammed after you, or you lose yourself in a maze and you can't get out—until you break out. But does that ever teach you a lesson? No! Instead of going ahead along the straight and narrow way, and keeping out of temptation, you halt at the very next gate you come to, just as though you had never seen a gate before, and exclaim: 'Now, this *is* a pretty garden, and *what* a neat white fence! I really must vault in and take a look round.' And so the whole thing is gone over again."

I confess there may be some truth in what he said, but the trouble I find with the straight and narrow way is that there's not room enough in it for two. And, then, it is only fair to me to say that some of the gardens were really most beautiful, and the shade very deep and sweet there, and the memories of the minutes I passed in them were very refreshing when I went back to the dust of the empty road. And no one, man or woman, can say that Royal Macklin ever trampled on the flowers, or broke the branches, or trespassed in another man's private grounds.

It was my cousin Beatrice who was responsible for the change of heart in me toward womankind. For very soon after she came to live with us, I noticed that in regard to all other young women I was growing daily more exacting. I did not admit this to myself, and still less to Beatrice, because she was most scornful of the girls I knew, and mocked at them. This was quite unfair of her, because she had no real acquaintance with them, and knew them only from photographs and tintypes, of which I had a most remarkable collection, and of what I chose to tell her about them. I was a good deal annoyed to find that the stories which appealed to me as best illustrating the character of each of my friends, only seemed to furnish Beatrice with fresh material for ridicule, and the girls of whom I said the least were the ones of whom she approved. The only girls of my acquaintance who also were friends of hers, were two sisters who lived at Dobbs Ferry, and whose father owned the greater part of it, and a yacht, in which he went down to his office every morning. But Beatrice held that my manner even to them was much too free and familiar, and that she could not understand why I did not see that it was annoying to them as well. I could not tell her in my own defence that their manner to me, when she was with us and when she was not, varied in a remarkable degree. It was not only girls who carried themselves differently before Beatrice : every man who met her seemed to try and show her the best in him, or at least to suppress any thought or act which might displease her. It was not that she was a prig, or an angel, but she herself was so fine and sincere, and treated all with such an impersonal and yet gracious manner that it became contagious, and everybody who met her imitated the model she unconsciously furnished. I was very much struck with this when she visited the Academy. Men who before her coming had seemed bold enough for any game, became dumb and embarrassed in her presence, and eventually it was the officers and instructors who escorted her over the grounds, while I and my acquaintances among the cadets formed a straggling rear-guard at her heels. On account of my grandfather, both she and my aunt were made much of by the Commandant and all the older officers, and when they continued to visit the Academy they were honored and welcomed for themselves, and I found that on such occasions my own popularity was enormously increased. I have always been susceptible to the opinion of others. Even when the reigning belle or the popular man of the class was not to me personally attractive, the fact that she was the reigning belle and that he was the man of the hour made me seek out the society of each. This was even so, when, as a matter of fact, I should have much preferred to dance with some less conspicuous beauty or talk with a more congenial companion. Consequently I began to value my cousin, whom I already regarded with the most tremendous admiration, for those lighter qualities which are common to all attractive girls, but which in my awe of her I had failed to recognize. There were many times, even, when I took myself by the shoulders and faced the question if I were not in love with Beatrice. I mean truly in love, with that sort of love that one does not talk about, even to one's self, certainly not to the girl. As the young man of the family, I had assumed the position of the heir of the house, and treated

Beatrice like a younger sister, but secretly I considered her in no such light.

Many nights when on post I would halt to think of her, and of her loveliness and high sincerity, and forget my duty while I stood with my arms crossed on the muzzle of my gun. In such moments the night, the silence, the moonlight piercing the summer leaves and falling at my feet, made me forget my promise to myself that I would never marry. I used to imagine then it was not the unlicked cubs under the distant tents I was protecting, but that I was awake to watch over and guard Beatrice, or that I was a knight, standing his vigil so that he might be worthy to wear the Red Cross and enter her service. In those lonely watches I saw littlenesses and meannesses in myself, which I could not see in the brisk light of day, and my self-confidence slipped from me and left me naked and abashed. I saw myself as a vain, swaggering boy, who, if he ever hoped to be a man among men, such as Beatrice was a woman above all other women, must change his nature at once and forever.

I was glad that I owed these good resolutions to her. I was glad that it was she who inspired them. Those nights, as I leaned on my gun, I dreamed even that it might end happily and beautifully in our marriage. I wondered if I could make her care, if I could ever be worthy of her, and I vowed hotly that I would love her as no other woman was ever loved.

And then I would feel the cold barrel of my musket pressing against the palm of my hand, or the bayonet would touch my cheek, and at the touch something would tighten in my throat, and I would shake the thoughts from me and remember that I was sworn to love only my country and my country's flag.

In my third year here my grandfather died. As the winter closed in he had daily grown more feeble, and sat hour after hour in his great arm-chair, dozing and dreaming, before the open fire. And one morning when he was alone in the room, Death, which had so often taken the man at his side, and stood at salute to let him live until his work was done, came to him and touched him gently. A few days later when his body passed through the streets of our little village, all the townspeople left their houses and shops, and stood in silent rows along the sidewalks, with their heads uncovered to the falling snow. Soldiers of his old regiments, now busy men of affairs in the great city below us, came to march behind him for the last time. Officers of the Loyal Legion, veterans of the Mexican War, regulars from Governor's Island, with their guns reversed, societies, political clubs, and strangers who knew him only by what he had done for his country, followed in the long procession as it wound its way through the cold, gray winter day to the side of the open grave. Until then I had not fully understood what it meant to me, for my head had been numbed and dulled; but as the body disappeared into the grave, and the slow notes of the bugle rose in the final call of "Lights out," I put my head on my aunt's shoulder and cried like a child. And I felt as though I were a child again, as I did when he came and sat beside my bed, and heard me say my prayers, and then closed the door behind him, leaving me in the darkness and alone.

But I was not entirely alone, for Beatrice was true and understanding; putting her own grief out of sight, caring for mine, and giving it the first place in her thoughts. For the next two days we walked for hours through the autumn woods where the dead leaves rustled beneath our feet, thinking and talking of him. Or for hours we would sit in silence, until the sun sank a golden red behind the wall of the Palisades, and we went back through the cold night to the open fireside and his empty chair.

Captain Macklin

St. Charles Hotel,
New Orleans

Six months ago had anyone told me that the day would come when I would feel thankful for the loss of my grandfather, I would have struck him. But for the last week I have been almost thankful that he is dead. The worst that could occur has happened. I am in bitter disgrace, and I am grateful that grandfather died before it came upon me. I have been dismissed from the Academy. The last of the "Fighting" Macklins has been declared unfit to hold the President's commission. I am cast out irrevocably; there is no appeal against the decision. I shall never change the gray for the blue. I shall never see the U. S. on my saddle-cloth, nor salute my country's flag as it comes fluttering down at sunset.

That I am on my way to try and redeem myself is only an attempt to patch up the broken pieces. The fact remains that the army has no use for me. I have been dismissed from West Point, in disgrace. It was a girl who brought it about, or rather my own foolishness over a girl. And before that there was much that led up to it. It is hard to write about it, but in these memoirs I mean to tell everything—the good, with the bad. And as I deserve no excuse, I make none.

During that winter, after the death of my

grandfather, and the spring which had followed, I tried hard to do well at the Point. I wanted to show them that though my grandfather was gone, his example and his wishes still inspired me. And though I was not a studious cadet, I was a smart soldier, and my demerits, when they came, were for smoking in my room or for breaking some other such silly rule, and never for slouching through the manual or coming on parade with my belts twisted. And at the end of the second year I had been promoted from corporal to be a cadet first sergeant, so that I was fourth in command over a company of seventy. Although this gave me the advantage of a light after "taps" until eleven o'clock, my day was so taken up with roll-calls, riding and evening drills and parade, that I never seemed to find time to cram my mechanics and chemistry, of which latter I could never see any possible benefit. How a knowledge of what acid will turn blue litmus-paper red is going to help an officer to find fodder for his troop horses, or inspire him to lead a forlorn hope, was then, and still is, beyond my youthful comprehension.

But these studies were down on the roster, and whether I thought well of them or not I was marked on them and judged accordingly. But I cannot claim that it was owing to them or my failure to understand them that my dismissai came, for, in spite of the absence of 3's in my markings and the abundance of 2's, I was still a soldierly cadet, and in spite of the fact that I was a stupid student, I made an excellent drill-master.

The trouble, when it came, was all my own making, and my dismissal was entirely due to an act of silly recklessness and my own idiocy. I had taken chances before and had not been caught; several times I ran the sentries at night for the sake of a noisy, drunken spree at a roadside tavern, and several times I had risked my chevrons because I did not choose to respect the arbitrary rules of the Academy which chafed my spirit and invited me to rebellion. It was not so much that I enjoyed those short hours of freedom, which I snatched in the face of such serious penalties, but it was the risk of the thing itself which attracted me, and which stirred the spirit of adventure that at times sways us all.

It was a girl who brought about my dismissal. I do not mean that she was in any way to blame, but she was the indirect cause of my leaving the Academy. It was a piece of fool's fortune, and I had not even the knowledge that I cared in the least for the girl to console me. She was only one of the several "piazza girls," as we called certain ones of those who were staying at Cranston's, with whom I had danced, to whom I had made pretty speeches, and had given the bell button that was sewn just over my heart. She certainly was not the best of them, for I can see now that she was vain and shallow, with a pert boldness, which I mistook for vivacity and wit. Three years ago, at the age of twenty, my knowledge of women was so complete that I divided them into six classes, and as soon as I met a new one I placed her in one of these classes and treated her according to the line of campaign I had laid down as proper for that class. Now, at twenty-three, I believe that there are as many different kinds of women as there are women, but that all kinds are good. Some women are better than others, but all are good, and all are different. This particular one unknowingly did me a great harm, but others have given me so much that is for good, that the balance side is in their favor. If a man is going to make a fool of himself, I personally would rather see him do it on account of a woman than for any other cause. For centuries Antony has been held up to the scorn of the world because he deserted his troops and his fleet, and sacrificed the Roman Empire for the sake of Cleopatra. Of course, that is the one thing a man cannot do, desert his men and betray his flag; but, if he is going to make a bad break in life, I rather like his doing it for the love of a woman. And, after all, it is rather fine to have for once felt something in you so great that you placed it higher than the Roman Empire.

I haven't the excuse of any great feeling in my case. She, the girl at Cranston's, was leaving the Point on the morrow, and she said if all I had sworn to her was true I would run the sentries that night to dance with her at the hop. Of course, love does not set tests nor ask sacrifices, but I had sworn that I had loved her, as I understood the world, and I told her I would come. I came, and I was recognized as I crossed the piazza to the ball-room. On the morning following I was called to the office of the Commandant and was told to pack my trunk. I was out of uniform in an hour, and that night at parade the order of the War Department dismissing me from the service was read to the assembled battalion.

I cannot write about that day. It was a very bright, beautiful day, full of life and sunshine, and I remember that I wondered how the world could be so cruel and unfeeling. The other second-classmen came in while I was packing my things, to say that they were sorry. They were kind enough; and some of them wanted me to go off to New York to friends of theirs and help upset it and get drunk. Their idea was, I suppose, to show the authorities how mistaken they had been in not making me an officer. But I could not be civil to any of them. I hated them all, and the place, and everyone in it. When I was dismissed my first thought was one of utter thankfulness that my grandfather died before the disgrace came upon me, and after that I did not much care. I was desperate and bitterly miserable. I knew, as the authorities could not know, that no one in my class felt more loyal to the service than myself; that I would have died twenty deaths for my country; that there was no one company post in the West, however distant from civilization, that would not have been a paradise to me; that there was no soldier in the army who would have served more devotedly than myself. And now I was found wanting and thrown out to herd with civilians, as unfit to hold the President's commission. After my first outbreak of impotent rage— for I blamed everyone but myself—remorse set in, and I thought of grandfather and of how much he had done for our country, and how we had talked so confidently together of the days when I would follow in his footsteps, as his grandchild, and as the son of " Fighting Macklin."

All my life I had talked and thought of nothing else, and now, just as I was within a year of it, I was shown the door which I never can enter again.

That it might be easier for us when I arrived, I telegraphed Beatrice what had happened, and when I reached the house the same afternoon she was waiting for me at the door, as though I was coming home for a holiday and it was all as it might have been. But neither of us was deceived, and without a word we walked out of the garden and up the hill to the woods where we had last been together six months before. Since then all had changed. Summer had come, the trees were heavy with leaves, and a warm haze hung over the river and the Palisades beyond. We seated ourselves on a fallen tree at the top of the hill and sat in silence, looking down into the warm, beautiful valley. It was Beatrice who was the first to speak.

" I have been thinking of what you can do," she began, gently, " and it seems to me, Royal, that what you need now is a good rest. It has been a hard winter for you. You have had to meet the two greatest trials that I hope will ever come to you. You took the first one well, as you should, and you will take this lesser one well also ; I know you will. But you must give yourself time to get over this—this disappointment, and to look about you. You must try to

We walked out to the woods.

content yourself at home with mother and with me. I am so selfish that I am almost glad it has happened, for now for a time we shall have you with us, all to ourselves, and we can take care of you and see that you are not gloomy and morbid. And then when the fall comes you will have decided what is best to do, and you will have a rest and a quiet summer with those who understand you and love you. And then you can go out into the world to do your work, whatever your work is to be."

I turned toward her and stared at her curiously.

"Whatever my work is to be," I repeated. "That was decided for me, Beatrice, when I was a little boy."

She returned my look for a moment in some doubt, and then leaned eagerly forward. "You mean to enlist?" she asked.

"To enlist? Not I!" I answered hotly. "If I'm not fit to be an officer now, I never shall be, at least not by that road. Do you know what it means? It's the bitterest life a man can follow. He is neither the one thing nor the other. The enlisted men suspect him, and the officers may not speak with him. I know one officer who got his commission that way. He swears now he would rather have served the time in jail. The officers at the post pointed him out to visitors, as the man who had failed at West Point, and who was working his way up from the ranks, and the men of his company thought that *he* thought, God help him, that he was too good for them, and made his life hell. Do you suppose I'd show my musket to men of my old mess, and have the girls I've danced with see me marching up and down a board walk with a gun on my shoulder? Do you see me going on errands for the men I've hazed, and showing them my socks and shirts at inspection so they can give me a good mark for being a clean and tidy soldier? No! I'll not enlist. If I'm not good enough to carry a sword I'm not good enough to carry a gun, and the United States Army can struggle along without me."

Beatrice shook her head.

"Don't say anything you'll be sorry for, Royal," she warned me.

"You don't understand," I interrupted. "I'm not saying anything against my own country or our army — how can I? I've proved clearly enough that I'm not fit for it. I'm only too grateful. I've had three years in the best military school in the world, at my country's expense, and I'm grateful. Yes, and I'm miserable, too, that I have failed to deserve it."

I stood up and straightened my shoulders. " But perhaps there are other countries less difficult to please," I said, "where I can lose myself and be forgotten, and where I can see service. After all, a soldier's business is to fight, not to sit at a post all day or to do a clerk's work at Washington."

Even as I spoke these chance words I seemed to feel the cloud of failure and disgrace passing from me. I saw vaguely a way to redeem myself, and, though I had spoken with bravado and at random, the words stuck in my mind, and my despondency fell from me like a heavy knapsack.

" Come," I said, cheerfully, " there can be no talk of a holiday for me until I have earned it. You know I would love to stay here now with you and Aunt in the old house, but I have no time to mope and be petted. If you fall down, you must not lie in the road and cry over your bruised shins ; you must pick yourself up and go on again, even if you are a bit sore and dirty."

We said nothing more, but my mind was made up, and when we reached the house I went at once to my room and repacked my trunk for a long journey. It was a leather trunk in which my grandfather used to carry his sword and uniform, and in it I now proudly placed the presenation sword he had bequeathed to me in his will, and my scanty wardrobe and $500 of the money he had left to me. All the rest of his fortune, with the exception of the $2,000 a year he had settled upon me, he had, I am glad to say, bequeathed with the house to Aunt Mary and Beatrice. When I had finished my packing I joined them at supper, and such was my elation at the prospect of at once setting forth to redeem myself, and to seek my fortune, that to me the meal passed most cheerfully. When it was finished, I found the paper of that morning, and spreading it out upon the table began a careful search in the foreign news for what tidings there might be of war.

I told Beatrice what I was doing, and without a word she brought out my old school atlas, and together under the light of the student-lamp we sought out the places mentioned in the foreign despatches, and discussed them, and the chances they might offer me.

There were, I remember, at the time that paper was printed, strained relations existing between France and China over the copper mines in Tonkin; there was a tribal war in Upper Burmah with native troops; there was a threat of complications in the Balkans, but the Balkans, as I have since learned, are always with us and always threatening. Nothing in the paper seemed to offer me the chance I sought, and apparently peace smiled on every other portion of the globe.

" There is always the mounted police in Canada," I said, tentatively.

" No," Beatrice answered, quietly, and without asking her reasons I accepted her decision and turned again to the paper. And then my eyes fell on a paragraph which at first I had overlooked—a modest, brief despatch tucked away in a corner, and unremarkable, except for its strange date-line. It was headed, " The Revolt in Honduras." I pointed to it with my finger, and Beatrice leaned forward with her head close to mine, and we read it together.

" Tegucigalpa, June 17th," it read. " The revolution here has assumed serious proportions. President Alvarez has proclaimed martial law over all provinces, and leaves to-morrow for Santa Barbara, where the Liberal forces under the rebel leader, ex-President Louis Garcia, were last in camp. General Laguerre is coming from Nicaragua to assist Garcia with his foreign legion of 200 men. He has seized the Nancy Miller, belonging to the Isthmian Line, and has fitted her with two Gatling guns. He is reported to be bombarding the towns on his way along the coast, and a detachment of Government troops is marching to Porto Cortez to prevent his landing. His force is chiefly composed of American and other aliens, who believe the overthrow of the present government will be beneficial to foreign residents."

" General Laguerre ! " I cried, eagerly, " that is not a Spanish name. General Laguerre must be a Frenchman. And it says that the men with him are Americans, and that the present government is against all foreigners."

I drew back from the table with a laugh, and stood smiling at Beatrice, but she shook her head, even though she smiled, too.

" Oh, not that," she said.

" My dear Beatrice," I expostulated, " it certainly isn't right that American interests in—what's the name of the place—in Honduras, should be jeopardized, is it ? And by an ignorant half-breed like this President What's-his-name ? Certainly not. It must be stopped, even if we have to requisition every steamer the Isthmian Line has afloat."

" Oh, Royal," Beatrice cried, " you are not serious. No, you wouldn't, you couldn't be so foolish. That's no affair of yours. That's not your country. Besides, that is not war; it is speculation. You are a gentleman, not a pirate and a filibuster."

"William Walker was a filibuster," I answered. "He took Nicaragua with 200 men and held it for two years against 20,000. I must begin somewhere," I cried, "why not there? A girl can't understand these things—at least, some girls can't—but I would have thought you would. What does it matter what I do or where I go?" I broke out, bitterly. "I have made a failure of my life at the very start. I am sick and sore and desperate. I don't care where I go or what——"

I would have ranted on for some time, no doubt, but that a look from Beatrice stopped me in mid-air, and I stood silent, feeling somewhat foolish.

"I can understand this much," she said, "that you are a foolish boy. How dare you talk of having made a failure of your life? Your life has not yet begun. You have yet to make it, and to show yourself something more than a boy." She paused, and then her manner changed, and she came toward me, looking up at me with eyes that were moist and softened with a sweet and troubled tenderness, and she took my hand and held it close in both of hers.

I had never seen her look more beautiful than she did at that moment. If it had been any other woman in the world but her, I would have caught her in my arms and kissed her again and again, but because it was she I could not touch her, but drew back and looked down into her eyes with the sudden great feeling I had for her. And so we stood for a moment, seeing each other as we had never seen each other before. And then she caught her breath quickly and drew away. But she turned her face toward me at once, and looked up at me steadily.

"I am so fond of you, Royal," she said, bravely, "you know, that—that I cannot bear to think of you doing anything in this world that is not fine and for the best. But if you will be a knight errant, and seek out dangers and fight windmills, promise me to be a true knight and that you will fight only when you must and only on the side that is just, and then you will come back bringing your sheaves with you."

I did not dare to look at her, but I raised her hand and held the tips of her fingers against my lips, and I promised, but I would have promised anything at that moment.

"If I am to be a knight," I said, and my voice sounded very hoarse and boyish, so that I hardly recognized it as my own, "you must give me your colors to wear on my lance, and if any other knight thinks his colors fairer, or the lady who gave them more lovely than you, I shall kill him."

She laughed softly and moved away.

"Of course," she said, "of course, you must kill him." She stepped a few feet from me, and, raising her hands to her throat, unfastened a little gold chain which she wore around her neck. She took it off and held it toward me. "Would you like this?" she said. I did not answer, nor did she wait for me to do so, but wound the chain around my wrist and fastened it, and I raised it and kissed it, and neither of us spoke. She went out to the veranda to warn her mother of my departure, and I to tell the servants to bring the carriage to the door.

A few minutes later, the suburban train drew out of the station at Dobbs Ferry, and I waved my hand to Beatrice as she sat in the carriage looking after me. The night was warm and she wore a white dress and her head was uncovered. In the smoky glare of the station lamps I could still see the soft tints of her hair; and as the train bumped itself together and pulled forward, I felt a sudden panic of doubt, a piercing stab at my heart, and something called on me to leap off the car that was bearing me away, and go back to the white figure sitting motionless in the carriage. As I gripped the iron railing to restrain myself, I felt the cold sweat springing to the palm of my hand. For a moment I forgot the end of my long journey. I saw it as something foolish, mad, fantastic. I was snatching at a flash of powder, when I could warm my hands at an open fire. I was deserting the one thing which counted and of which I was certain; the one thing I loved. And then the train turned a curve, the lamps of the station and the white ghostly figure were shut from me, and I entered the glaring car filled with close air and smoke and smelling lamps. I seated myself beside a window and leaned far out into the night, so that the wind of the rushing train beat in my face.

And in a little time the clanking car-wheels seemed to speak to me, beating out the words brazenly so that I thought everyone in the car must hear them.

"Turn again, turn again, Royal Macklin," they seemed to say to me. "She loves you, Royal Macklin, she loves you, she loves you."

And I thought of Dick Whittington when the Bow bells called to him, as he paused in the country lane to look back at the smoky roof of London, and they had offered him so little, while for me the words seemed to promise the proudest place a man could hold. And I imagined myself still at home, working by day in some New York office and coming back by night to find Beatrice at the station waiting for me, always in a white dress, and with her brown hair glowing in the light of the lamps. And I pictured us taking long walks together above the Hudson, and quiet, happy evenings by the fireside. But the rhythm of the car-wheels altered, and from " She loves you, she loves you," the refrain now came brokenly and fiercely, like the reports of muskets fired in hate and fear, and mixed with their roar and rattle I seemed to distinguish words of command in a foreign tongue, and the groans of men wounded and dying. And I saw, rising above great jungles and noisome swamps, a long mountain-range piercing a burning, naked sky; and in a pass in the mountains a group of my own countrymen, ragged and worn and with eyes lit with fever, waving a strange flag, and beset on every side by dark-faced soldiers, and I saw my own face among them, hollow-cheeked and tanned, with my head bandaged in a scarf; I felt the hot barrel of a rifle burning my palm, I smelt the pungent odor of spent powder, my throat and nostrils were assailed with smoke. I suffered all the fierce joy and agony of battle, and the picture of the white figure of Beatrice grew dim and receded from me, and as it faded the eyes regarded me wistfully and reproached me, but I would not heed them, but turned my own eyes away. And again I saw the menacing negro faces and the burning sunlight and the strange flag that tossed and whimpered in the air above my head, the strange flag of unknown, tawdry colors, like the painted face of a woman in the street, but a flag at which I cheered and shouted as though it were my own, as though I loved it; a flag for which I would fight and die.

The train twisted its length into the great station, the men about me rose and crowded down the aisle, and I heard the cries of newsboys and hackmen and jangling car-bells, and all the roar and tumult of a great city at night.

But I had already made my choice. Within an hour I had crossed to the Jersey side, and was speeding south, south toward New Orleans, toward the Gulf of Mexico, toward Honduras, to Colonel Laguerre and his foreign legion.

II

S. S. PANAMA,
OFF COAST OF HONDURAS

TO one who never before had travelled farther
than is Dobbs Ferry from Philadelphia, my
journey south to New Orleans was something in
the way of an expedition, and I found it rich in
incident and adventure. Everything was new
and strange, but nothing was so strange as my
own freedom. After three years of discipline, of
going to bed by drum-call, of waking by drum-
call, and obeying the orders of others, this new
independence added a supreme flavor to all my
pleasures. I took my journey very seriously,
and I determined to make every little incident
contribute to my better knowledge of the world.
I rated the chance acquaintances of the smoking-
car as aids to a clear understanding of mankind,
and when at Washington I saw above the house-
tops the marble dome of the Capitol I was thrilled
to think that I was already so much richer in experience.

To me the country through which we passed
spoke with but one meaning. I saw it as the

chess-board of the War of the Rebellion. I imagined the towns fortified and besieged, the hills topped with artillery, the forests alive with troops in ambush, and in my mind, on account of their strategic value to the enemy, I destroyed the bridges over which we passed. The passengers were only too willing to instruct a stranger in the historical values of their country. They pointed out to me where certain regiments had camped, where homesteads had been burned, and where real battles, not of my own imagining, but which had cost the lives of many men, had been lost and won. I found that to these chance acquaintances the events of which they spoke were as fresh after twenty years as though they had occurred but yesterday, and they accepted my curiosity as only a natural interest in a still vital subject. I judged it advisable not to mention that General Hamilton was my grandfather. Instead I told them that I was the son of an officer who had died for the cause of secession. This was the first time I had ever missed an opportunity of boasting of my relationship to my distinguished grandparent, and I felt meanly conscious that I was in a way disloyal. But they were so genuinely pleased when they learned that my father had fought for the South, that I lacked the courage to tell them that while he was so engaged another relative of mine had driven one of their best generals through three States.

I am one who makes the most of what he sees, and even the simplest things filled me with delight; my first sight of cotton-fields, of tobacco growing in the leaf, were great moments to me; and that the men who guarded the negro convicts at work in the fields still clung to the uniform of gray, struck me as a fact of pathetic interest.

I was delayed in New Orleans for only one day. At the end of that time I secured passage on the steamer Panama. She was listed to sail for Aspinwall at nine o'clock the next morning, and to touch at ports along the Central American coast. While waiting for my steamer I mobilized my transport and supplies, and purchased such articles as I considered necessary for a rough campaign in a tropical climate. My purchases consisted of a revolver, a money-belt, in which to carry my small fortune, which I had exchanged into gold double-eagles, a pair of field-glasses, a rubber blanket, a canteen, riding boots, and saddle-bags. I decided that my uniform and saddle would be furnished me from the quartermaster's department of Garcia's army, for in my ignorance I supposed I was entering on a campaign conducted after the methods of European armies.

We left the levees of New Orleans early in the

morning, and for the remainder of the day steamed slowly down the Mississippi River. I sat alone upon the deck watching the low, swampy banks slipping past us on either side, the gloomy cypress-trees heavy with gray moss, the abandoned cotton-gins and disused negro quarters. As I did so a feeling of homesickness and depression came upon me, and my disgraceful failure at the Point, the loss of my grandfather, and my desertion of Beatrice, for so it began to seem to me, filled me with a bitter melancholy.

The sun set the first day over great wastes of swamp, swamp-land, and pools of inky black, which stretched as far as the eye could reach ; gloomy, silent, and barren of any form of life. It was a picture which held neither the freedom of the open sea nor the human element of the solid earth. It seemed to me as though the world must have looked so when darkness brooded over the face of the waters, and as I went to my berth that night I felt as though I were saying good-by forever to all that was dear to me—my country, my home, and the girl I loved.

I was awakened in the morning by a motion which I had never before experienced. I was being gently lifted and lowered and rolled to and fro as a hammock is rocked by the breeze. For some minutes I lay between sleep and waking, struggling back to consciousness, until with a sudden gasp of delight it came to me that at last I was at sea. I scrambled from my berth and pulled back the curtains of the air port. It was as though over night the ocean had crept up to my window. It stretched below me in great distances of a deep, beautiful blue. Tumbling waves were chasing each other over it, and millions of white caps glanced and flashed as they raced by me in the sun. It was my first real view of the ocean, and the restlessness of it and the freedom of it stirred me with a great happiness. I drank in its beauty as eagerly as I filled my lungs with the keen salt air, and thanked God for both.

The three short days which followed were full of new and delightful surprises, some because it was all so strange and others because it was so exactly what I had hoped it would be. I had read many tales of the sea, but ships I knew only as they moved along the Hudson at the end of the towing-line. I had never felt one rise and fall beneath me, nor from the deck of one watched the sun sink into the water. I had never at night looked up at the great masts, and seen them swing, like a pendulum reversed, between me and the stars.

There was so much to learn that was new and so many things to see on the waters, and in the skies, that it seemed wicked to sleep. So, during nearly the whole of every night, I stood with Captain Leeds on his bridge, or asked ignorant questions of the man at the wheel. The steward of the Panama was purser, supercargo, and bar-keeper in one, and a most interesting man. He apparently never slept, but at any hour was will-ing to sit and chat with me. It was he who first introduced me to the wonderful mysteries of the alligator pear as a salad, and taught me to prefer, in a hot country, Jamaica rum with half a lime squeezed into the glass to all other spirits. It was a most educational trip.

I had much entertainment on board the Pana-ma by pretending that I was her captain, and that she was sailing under my orders. Sometimes I pretended that she was an American man-of-war, and sometimes a filibuster escaping from an American man-of-war. This may seem an absurd and childish game, but I had always wanted to hold authority, and as I had never done so, ex-cept as a drill sergeant at the Academy, it was my habit to imagine myself in whatever position of responsibility my surroundings suggested. For this purpose the Panama served me excellently, and in scanning the horizon for hostile fleets or a pirate flag I was as conscientious as was the lookout in the bow. At the Academy I had often sat in my room with maps spread out before me planning attacks on the enemy, considering my lines of communication, telegraphing wildly for reinforcements, and despatching my aides with a clearly written, comprehensive order to where my advance column was engaged. I believe this "play-acting," as my room-mate used to call it, helped me to think quickly, to give an intelligent command intelligently, and made me rich in resources.

For the first few days I was so enchanted with my new surroundings that the sinister purpose of my journey South lost its full value. And when, as we approached Honduras, it was recalled to me, I was surprised to find that I had heard no one on board discuss the war, nor refer to it in any way. When I considered this, I was the more surprised because Porto Cortez was one of the chief ports at which we touched, and I was annoyed to find that I had travelled so far for the sake of a cause in which those directly interested felt so little concern. I set about with great caution to discover the reason for this lack of interest. The passengers of the Panama came from widely different parts of Central America. They were coffee planters and mining engineers, concession hunters, and promoters of mining companies. I sounded each of them separately as to the condition of affairs in Honduras, and gave as my reason for inquiring the fact that I had thoughts of investing my money there. I talked rather largely of my money. But this information, instead of inducing them to speak of Honduras, only made each of them more eloquent in praising the particular republic in which his own money was invested, and each begged me to place mine with his. In the course of one day I was offered a part ownership in four coffee plantations, a rubber forest, a machine for turning the sea-turtles into fat and shell, and the good-will and fixtures of a dentist's office.

Except that I obtained some reputation on board as a young man of property, which reputation I endeavored to maintain by treating everyone to drinks in the social hall, my inquiries led to no result. No one apparently knew, nor cared to know, of the revolution in Honduras, and passed it over as a joke. This hurt me, but lest they should grow suspicious, I did not continue my inquiries.

THE CAFÉ SANTOS,
SAGUA LA GRANDE, HONDURAS

We sighted land at seven in the morning, and as the ship made in toward the shore I ran to the bow and stood alone peering over the rail. Before me lay the scene set for my coming adventures, and as the ship threaded the coral reefs, my excitement ran so high that my throat choked, and my eyes suddenly dimmed with tears. It seemed too good to be real. It seemed impossible that it could be true; that at last I should be about to act the life I had so long only rehearsed and pretended. But the pretence had changed to something living and actual. In front of me, under a flashing sun, I saw the palm-fringed harbor of my dreams, a white village of thatched mud houses, a row of ugly huts above which drooped limply the flags of foreign consuls, and, far beyond, a deep blue range of mountains, forbidding and mysterious, rising out of a steaming swamp into a burning sky, and on the harbor's only pier, in blue drill uniforms and gay red caps, a group of dark-skinned, swaggering soldiers. This hot, volcano-looking land was the one I had come to free from its fetters. These swarthy barefooted brigands were the men with whom I was to fight.

My trunk had been packed and strapped since sunrise, and before the ship reached the pier, I had said "good-by" to everyone on board and was waiting impatiently at the gang-way. I was the only passenger to leave, and no cargo was unloaded nor taken on. She was waiting only for the agent of the company to confer with Captain Leeds, and while these men were conversing on the bridge, and the hawser was being drawn on board, the custom-house officers, much to my disquiet, began to search my trunk. I had nothing with me which was dutiable, but my grandfather's presentation sword was hidden in the trunk and its presence there and prospective use would be difficult to explain. It was accordingly with a feeling of satisfaction that I noticed on a building on the end of the pier the sign of our consulate and the American flag, and that a young man, evidently an American, was hurrying from it toward the ship. But as it turned out I had no need of his services, for I had concealed the sword so cleverly by burying each end of it in one of my long cavalry boots, that the official failed to find it.

I had locked my trunk again and was waving final farewells to those on the Panama, when the young man from the consulate began suddenly to race down the pier, shouting as he came.

The gang-way had been drawn up, and the steamer was under way, churning the water as she swung slowly seaward, but she was still within easy speaking distance of the pierhead.

The young man rushed through the crowd, jostling the native Indians and negro soldiers, and shrieked at the departing vessel.

"Stop!" he screamed, "stop! stop her!"

He recognized Captain Leeds on the bridge,

and, running along the pierhead until he was just below it, waved wildly at him.

"Where's my freight?" he cried. "My freight! You haven't put off my freight."

Captain Leeds folded his arms comfortably upon the rail, and regarded the young man calmly and with an expression of amusement.

"Where are my sewing-machines?" the young man demanded. "Where are the sewing-machines invoiced me by this steamer?"

"Sewing-machines, Mr. Aiken?" the Captain answered. "I left your sewing-machines in New Orleans."

"You what?" shrieked the young man. "You left them?"

"I left them sitting on the company's levee," the Captain continued, calmly. "The revenue officers have 'em by now, Mr. Aiken. Some parties said they weren't sewing-machines at all. They said you were acting for Laguerre."

The ship was slowly drawing away. The young man stretched out one arm as though to detain her, and danced frantically along the stringhead.

"How dare you!" he cried. "I'm a commission merchant. I deal in whatever I please—and I'm the American Consul!"

The Captain laughed, and with a wave of his hand in farewell backed away from the rail.

"That may be," he shouted, "but this line isn't carrying freight for General Laguerre, nor for you, neither." He returned and made a speaking trumpet of his hands. "Tell him from me," he shouted, mockingly, "that if he wants his sewing-machines he'd better go North and steal 'em. Same as he stole our Nancy Miller."

The young man shook both his fists in helpless anger.

"You damned banana trader," he shrieked, "you'll lose your license for this. I'll fix you for this. I'll dirty your card for you, you pirate!"

The Captain flung himself far over the rail. He did not need a speaking trumpet now—his voice would have carried above the tumult of a hurricane.

"You'll what?" he roared. "You'll dirty my card, you thieving filibuster? Do you know what I'll do to you? I'll have your tin sign taken away from you, before I touch this port again. You'll see—you—you—" he ended impotently for lack of epithets, but continued in eloquent pantomime to wave his arms.

With an oath the young man recognized defeat, and shrugged his shoulders.

"Oh, you go to the devil," he shouted, and turned away. He saw me observing him, and as I was the only person present who looked as though he understood English, he grinned at me sheepishly, and nodded.

"I don't care for him," he said. "He can't frighten me."

I considered this as equivalent to an introduction.

"You are the United States Consul?" I asked. The young man nodded briskly.

"Yes; I am. Where do you come from?"

"Dobbs Ferry, near New York," I answered. "I'd—I'd like to have a talk with you, when you are not busy."

"That's all right," he said. "I'm not busy now. That bumboat pirate queered the only business I had. Where are you going to stop? There is only one place," he explained; "that's Pulido's. He'll knife you if he thinks you have five dollars in your belt, and the bar-room is half under water anyway. Or you can take a cot in my shack, if you like, and I'll board and lodge you for two pesos a day—that's one dollar in our money. And if you are going up country," he went on, "I can fit you out with mules and mozos and everything you want, from canned meats to an escort of soldiers. You're sure to be robbed anyway," he urged, pleasantly, "and you might as well give the job to a fellow-countryman. I'd hate to have one of these greasers get it."

"You're welcome to try," I said, laughing.

In spite of his manner, which was much too familiar and patronizing, the young man amused me, and I must confess moreover that at that moment I felt very far from home and was glad to meet an American, and one not so much older than myself. The fact that he was our consul struck me as a most fortunate circumstance.

He clapped his hands and directed one of the negroes to carry my trunk to the consulate, and I walked with him up the pier, the native soldiers saluting him awkwardly as he passed. He returned their salute with a flourish, and more to impress me I guessed than from any regard for them.

"That's because I'm Consul," he said, with satisfaction. "There's only eight white men in Porto Cortez," he explained, "and we're all consular agents. The Italian consular agent is a Frenchman, and an Italian, Guessippi—the Banana King, they call him—is consular agent for both Germany and England, and the only German here is consular agent for France and Holland. You see, each of 'em has to represent some other country than his own, because his country knows why he left it." He threw back his head and laughed at this with great delight. Apparently he had already forgotten the rebuff from Captain Leeds. But it had made a deep impression upon me. I had heard Leeds virtually accuse the consul of being an agent of General Laguerre, and I suspected that the articles he had refused to deliver were more likely to be machine guns than sewing-machines. If this were true, Mr. Aiken was a person in whom I could confide with safety.

The consulate was a one-story building of corrugated iron, hot, unpainted, and unlovely. It was set on wooden logs to lift it from the reach of "sand jiggers" and the surf, which at high tide ran up the beach, under and beyond it. Inside it was rude and bare, and the heat and the smell of the harbor, and of the swamp on which the town was built, passed freely through the open doors.

Aiken proceeded to play the host in a most cordial manner. He placed my trunk in the room I was to occupy, and set out some very strong Hondurian cigars and a bottle of Jamaica rum. While he did this he began to grumble over the loss of his sewing-machines, and to swear picturesquely at Captain Leeds, bragging of the awful things he meant to do to him But when he had tasted his drink and lighted a cigar, his good-humor returned, and he gave his attention to me.

Captain Macklin

"Now then, young one," he asked, in a tone of the utmost familiarity, "what's your trouble?"

I explained that I could not help but hear what the Captain shouted at him from the Panama, and I asked if it was contrary to the law of Honduras for one to communicate with the officer Captain Leeds had mentioned—General Laguerre.

"The old man, hey?" Aiken exclaimed and stared at me apparently with increased interest. "Well, there are some people who might prevent your getting to him," he answered, diplomatically. For a moment he sipped his rum and water, while he examined me from over the top of the cup. Then he winked and smiled.

"Come now," he said, encouragingly. "Speak up. What's the game? You can trust me. You're an agent for Collins, or the Winchester Arms people, aren't you?"

"On the contrary," I said, with some haughtiness, "I am serving no one's interest but my own. I read in the papers of General Laguerre and his foreign legion, and I came here to join him and to fight with him. That's all. I am a soldier of fortune, I said." I repeated this with some emphasis, for I liked the sound of it. "I am a soldier of fortune, and my name is Macklin. I hope in time to make it better known."

"A soldier of fortune, hey?" exclaimed Aiken, observing me with a grin. "What soldiering have you done?"

I replied, with a little embarrassment, that as yet I had seen no active service, but that for three years I had been trained for it at West Point.

"At West Point, the deuce you have!" said Aiken. His tone was now one of respect, and he regarded me with marked interest. He was not a gentleman, but he was sharp-witted enough to recognize one in me, and my words and bearing had impressed him. Still his next remark was disconcerting.

"But if you're a West Point soldier," he asked, "why the devil do you want to mix up in a shooting-match like this?"

I was annoyed, but I answered, civilly: "It's in a good cause," I said. "As I understand the situation, this President Alvarez is a tyrant. He's opposed to all progress. It's a fight for liberty."

Aiken interrupted me with a laugh, and placed his feet on the table.

"Oh, come," he said, in a most offensive tone. "Play fair, play fair."

"Play fair? What do you mean?" I demanded.

"You don't expect me to believe," he said, jeeringly, " that you came all the way down here, just to fight for the sacred cause of liberty."

I may occasionally exaggerate a bit in representing myself to be a more important person than I really am, but if I were taught nothing else at the Point, I was taught to tell the truth, and when Aiken questioned my word I felt the honor of the whole army rising within me and stiffening my back-bone.

" You had better believe what I tell you, sir," I answered him, sharply. " You may not know it, but you are impertinent ! "

I have seldom seen a man so surprised as was Aiken when I made this speech. His mouth opened and remained open while ʌe slowly removed his feet from the table and allowed the legs of his chair to touch the floor.

" Great Scott," he said at last, " but you have got a nasty temper. I'd forgotten that folks are so particular."

" Particular—because I object to having my word doubted," I asked. " I must request you to send my trunk to Pulido's. I fancy you and I won't hit it off together." I rose and started to leave the room, but he held out his hands to prevent me, and exclaimed, in consternation :

" Oh, that's no way to treat me," he protested.

"I didn't say anything for you to get on your ear about. If I did, I'm sorry." He stepped forward, offering to shake my hand, and as I took his doubtfully, he pushed me back into my chair.

"You mustn't mind me," he went on. "It's been so long since I've seen a man from God's country that I've forgotten how to do the polite. Here, have another drink and start even." He was so eager and so suddenly humble that I felt ashamed of my display of offended honor, and we began again with a better understanding.

I told him once more why I had come, and this time he accepted my story as though he considered my wishing to join Laguerre the most natural thing in the world, nodding his head and muttering approvingly. When I had finished he said, "You may not think so now, but I guess you've come to the only person who can help you. If you'd gone to anyone else you'd probably have landed in jail." He glanced over his shoulder at the open door, and then, after a mysterious wink at me, tiptoed out upon the veranda, and ran rapidly around and through the house. This precaution on his part gave me a thrill of satisfaction. I felt that at last I was a real conspirator that I was concerned in something dangerous and weighty. I sipped at my glass with an air of indifference, but as a matter of fact I was rather nervous.

"You can't be too careful," Aiken said as he reseated himself. "Of course, the whole thing is a comic opera, but if they suspect you are working against them, they're just as likely as not to make it a tragedy, with you in the star part. Now I'll explain how I got into this, and I can assure you it wasn't through any love of liberty with me. The consular agent here is a man named Quay, and he and I have been in the commission business together. About three months ago, when Laguerre was organizing his command at Bluefields, Garcia, who is the leader of the revolutionary party, sent word down here to Quay to go North for him and buy two machine guns and invoice 'em to me at the consulate. Quay left on the next steamer and appointed me acting consul, but except for his saying so I've no more real authority to act as consul than you have. The plan was that when Laguerre captured this port he would pick up the guns and carry them on to Garcia. Laguerre was at Bluefields, but couldn't get into the game for lack of a boat. So when the Nancy Miller touched there he and his crowd boarded her just like a lot of old-fashioned pirates and turned the passengers out on the wharf. Then they put a gun at the head of the engineer and ordered him to take them back to Porto Cortez. But when they reached here the guns hadn't arrived from New Orleans. And so, after a bit of a fight on landing, Laguerre pushed on without them to join Garcia. He left instructions with me to bring him word when they arrived. He's in hiding up there in the mountains, waiting to hear from me now. They ought to have come this steamer day on the Panama along with you, but, as you know, they didn't. I never thought they would. I knew the Isthmian Line people wouldn't carry 'em. They've got to beat Garcia, and until this row is over they won't even carry a mail-bag for fear he might capture it."

"Is that because General Laguerre seized one of their steamers?" I asked.

"No, it's an old fight," said Aiken, "and Laguerre's stealing the Nancy Miller was only a part of it. The fight began between Garcia and the Isthmian Line when Garcia became president. He tried to collect some money from the Isthmian Line, and old man Fiske threw him out of the palace and made Alvarez president."

I was beginning to find the politics of the revolution into which I had precipitated myself somewhat involved, and I suppose I looked puzzled, for Aiken laughed.

Captain Macklin

"You can laugh," I said, "but it is rather confusing. Who is Fiske? Is he another revolutionist?"

"Fiske!" exclaimed Aiken. "Don't tell me you don't know who Fiske is? I mean old man Fiske, the Wall Street banker—Joseph Fiske, the one who owns the steam yacht and all the railroads."

I had of course heard of that Joseph Fiske, but his name to me was only a word meaning money. I had never thought of Joseph Fiske as a human being. At school and at the Point when we wanted to give the idea of wealth that could not be counted we used to say, "As rich as Joe Fiske." But I answered, in a tone that suggested that I knew him intimately:

"Oh, that Fiske," I said. "But what has he to do with Honduras?"

"He owns it," Aiken answered. "It's like this," he began. "You must understand that almost every republic in Central America is under the thumb of a big trading firm or a banking house or a railroad. For instance, all these revolutions you read about in the papers—it's seldom they start with the people. The *pueblo* don't often elect a president or turn one out. That's generally the work of a New York business firm that wants a concession. If the president in office

74

won't give it a concession the company starts out to find one who will. It hunts up a rival politician or a general of the army who wants to be president, and all of them do, and makes a deal with him. It promises him if he'll start a revolution it will back him with the money and the guns. Of course, the understanding is that if the leader of the fake revolution gets in he'll give his New York backers whatever they're after. Sometimes they want a concession for a railroad, and sometimes it's a nitrate bed or a rubber forest, but you can take my word for it that there's very few revolutions down here that haven't got a money-making scheme at the bottom of them.

"Now this present revolution was started by the Isthmian Steamship Line, of which Joe Fiske is president. It runs its steamers from New Orleans to the Isthmus of Panama. In its original charter this republic gave it the monopoly of the fruit-carrying trade from all Hondurian ports. In return for this the company agreed to pay the government $10,000 a year and ten per cent. on its annual receipts, if the receipts ever exceeded a certain amount. Well, curiously enough, although the line has been able to build seven new steamers, its receipts have never exceeded that fixed amount. And if you know

these people the reason for that is very simple.
The company has always given each succeeding
president a lump sum for himself, on the condition that he won't ask any impertinent questions about the company's earnings. Its people
tell him that it is running at a loss, and he always
takes their word for it. But Garcia, when he
came in, either was too honest, or they didn't
pay him enough to keep quiet. I don't know
which it was, but, anyway, he sent an agent to
New Orleans to examine the company's books.
The agent discovered the earnings have been so
enormous that by rights the Isthmian Line owed
the government of Honduras $500,000. This
was a great chance for Garcia, and he told them
to put up the back pay or lose their charter.
They refused and he got back at them by pre-
venting their ships from taking on any cargo in
Honduras, and by seizing their plant here and at
Truxillo. Well, the company didn't dare to go
to law about it, nor appeal to the State Department, so it started a revolution. It picked out a
thief named Alvarez as a figure-head and helped
him to bribe the army and capture the capital.
Then he bought a decision from the local courts
in favor of the company. After that there was
no more talk about collecting back pay. Garcia
was an exile in Nicaragua. There he met La-

guerre, who is a professional soldier of fortune, and together they cooked up this present revolution. They hope to put Garcia back into power again. How he'll act if he gets in I don't know. The common people believe he's a patriot, that he'll keep all the promises he makes them—and he makes a good many—and some white people believe in him, too. Laguerre believes in him, for instance. Laguerre told me that Garcia was a second Bolivar and Washington. But he might be both of them, and he couldn't beat the Isthmian Line. You see, while he has prevented the Isthmian Line from carrying bananas, he's cut off his own nose by shutting off his only source of supply. For these big corporations hang together at times, and on the Pacific side the Pacific Mail Company has got the word from Fiske, and they won't carry supplies, either. That's what I meant by saying that Joe Fiske owns Honduras. He's cut it off from the world, and only *his* arms and *his* friends can get into it. And the joke of it is he can't get out."

"Can't get out?" I exclaimed. "What do you mean?"

"Why, he's up there at Tegucigalpa himself," said Aiken. "Didn't you know that? He's up at the capital, visiting Alvarez. He came in through this port about two weeks ago."

Captain Macklin

"Joseph Fiske is fighting in a Hondurian revolution?" I exclaimed.

"Certainly not!" cried Aiken. "He's here on a pleasure trip; partly pleasure, partly business. He came here on his yacht. You can see her from the window, lying to the left of the buoy. Fiske has nothing to do with this row. I don't suppose he knows there's a revolution going on."

I resented this pretended lack of interest on the part of the Wall Street banker. I condemned it as a piece of absurd affectation.

"Don't you believe it!" I said. "No matter how many millions a man has, he doesn't stand to lose $500,000 without taking an interest in it."

"Oh, but he doesn't know about *that*," said Aiken. "He doesn't know the ins and outs of the story—what I've been telling you. That's on the inside—that's café scandal. That side of it would never reach him. I suppose Joe Fiske is president of a *dozen* steamship lines, and all he does is to lend his name to this one, and preside at board meetings. The company's lawyers tell him whatever they think he ought to know. They probably say they're having trouble down here owing to one of the local revolutions, and that Garcia is trying to blackmail them."

"Then you don't think Fiske came down here about this?" I asked.

"About this?" repeated Aiken, in a tone of such contempt that I disliked him intensely. For the last half hour Aiken had been jumping unfeelingly on all my ideals and illusions.

"No," he went on. "He came here on his yacht on a pleasure trip around the West India Islands, and he rode in from here to look over the Copan Silver Mines. Alvarez is terribly keen to get rid of him. He's afraid the revolutionists will catch him and hold him for ransom. He'd bring a good price," Aiken added, reflectively. "It's enough to make a man turn brigand. And his daughter, too. She'd bring a good price."

"His daughter!" I exclaimed.

Aiken squeezed the tips of his fingers together, and kissed them, tossing the imaginary kiss up toward the roof. Then he drank what was left of his rum and water at a gulp and lifted the empty glass high in the air. "To the daughter," he said.

It was no concern of mine, but I resented his actions exceedingly. I think I was annoyed that he should have seen the young lady while I had not. I also resented his toasting her before a stranger. I knew he could not have met her, and his pretence of enthusiasm made him appear quite ridiculous. He looked at me mournfully, shaking his head as though it were impossible for him to give me an idea of her.

79

"Why they say," he exclaimed, "that when she rides along the trail, the native women kneel beside it.

"She's the best looking girl I ever saw," he declared, "and she's a thoroughbred too!" he added, "or she wouldn't have stuck it out in this country when she had a clean yacht to fall back on. She's been riding around on a mule, so they tell me, along with her father and the engineering experts, and just as though she enjoyed it. The men up at the mines say she tired them all out."

I had no desire to discuss the young lady with Aiken, so I pretended not to be interested, and he ceased speaking, and we smoked in silence. But my mind was nevertheless wide awake to what he had told me. I could not help but see the dramatic values which had been given to the situation by the presence of this young lady. The possibilities were tremendous. Here was I, fighting against her father, and here was she, beautiful and an heiress to many millions. In the short space of a few seconds I had pictured myself rescuing her from brigands, denouncing her father for not paying his honest debt to Honduras, had been shot down by his escort, Miss Fiske had bandaged my wounds, and I was returning North as her prospective husband on my prospective father-in-law's yacht. Aiken aroused me from this by rising to his feet. " Now then," he said, briskly, " if you want to go to Laguerre you can come with me. I've got to see him to explain why his guns haven't arrived, and I'll take you with me." He made a wry face and laughed. " A nice welcome he'll give me," he said. I jumped to my feet. " There's my trunk," I said; " it's ready, and so am I. When do we start ? "

" As soon as it is moonlight," Aiken answered.

The remainder of the day was spent in preparing for our journey. I was first taken to the commandante and presented to him as a commercial traveller. Aiken asked him for a passport permitting me to proceed to the capital " for purposes of trade." As consular agent Aiken needed no passport for himself, but to avoid suspicion he informed the commandante that his object in visiting Tegucigalpa was to persuade Joseph Fiske, as president of the Isthmian Line, to place buoys in the harbor of Porto Cortez and give the commission for their purchase to the commandante. Aiken then and always was the most graceful liar I have ever met. His fictions were never for his own advantage, at least not obviously so. Instead, they always held out some pleasing hope for the person to whom they were addressed. His plans and promises as to what he would do were so alluring that even when I knew he was lying I liked to pretend that he was not. This particular fiction so interested the commandante that he even offered us an escort of soldiers, which honor we naturally declined.

That night when the moon had risen we started inland, each mounted on a stout little mule, and followed by a third, on which was swung my trunk, balanced on the other side by Aiken's saddle bags. A Carib Indian whom Aiken had selected because of his sympathies for the revolution walked beside the third mule and directed its progress by the most startling shrieks and howls. To me it was a most memorable and marvellous night, and although for the greater part of it Aiken dozed in his saddle and woke only to abuse his mule, I was never more wakeful nor more happy. At the very setting forth I was pleasantly stirred when at the limit of the town a squad of soldiers halted us and demanded our passports. This was my first encounter with the government troops. They were barefooted and most slovenly looking soldiers, mere boys in age and armed with old-fashioned Remingtons. But their officer, the captain of the guard, was more smartly dressed, and I was delighted to find that my knowledge of Spanish, in which my grandfather had so persistently drilled me, enabled me to understand all that passed between him and Aiken. The captain warned us that the revolutionists were camped along the trail, and that if challenged we had best answer quickly that we were Americanos. He also told us that General Laguerre and his legion of "gringoes" were in hiding in the highlands some two days' ride from the coast. Aiken expressed the greatest concern at this, and was for at once turning back. His agitation was so convincing, he was apparently so frightened, that, until he threw a quick wink at me, I confess I was completely taken in. For some time he refused to be calmed, and it was only when the captain assured him that his official position would protect him from any personal danger that he consented to ride on. Before we crossed the town limits he had made it quite evident that the officer himself was solely responsible for his continuing on his journey, and he denounced Laguerre and all his works with a picturesqueness of language and a sincerity that filled me with confusion. I even began to doubt if after all Aiken was not playing a game for both sides, and might not end my career by leading me into a trap. After we rode on I considered the possibility of this quite seriously, and I was not reassured until I heard the *mozo*, with many chuckles and shrugs of the shoulder, congratulate Aiken on the way he had made a fool of the captain.

"That's called diplomacy, José," Aiken told him. "That's my statecraft. It's because I have so much statecraft that I am a consul. You keep your eye on this American consul, José, and you'll learn a lot of statecraft."

José showed his teeth and grinned, and after he had dropped into a line behind us we could hear him still chuckling.

"You would be a great success in secret service work, Aiken," I said, "or on the stage."

We were riding in single file, and in order to see my face in the moonlight he had to turn in his saddle.

"And yet I didn't," he laughed.

"What do you mean," I asked, "were you ever a spy or an actor?"

"I was both," he said. "I was a failure at both, too. I got put in jail for being a spy, and I ought to have been hung for my acting." I kicked my mule forward in order to hear better.

"Tell me about it," I asked, eagerly. "About when you were a spy."

But Aiken only laughed, and rode on without turning his head.

"You wouldn't understand," he said after a

pause. Then he looked at me over his shoulder. "It needs a big black background of experience and hard luck to get the perspective on that story," he explained. "It wouldn't appeal to you; you're too young. They're some things they don't teach at West Point."

"They teach us," I answered, hotly, "that if we're detailed to secret service work we are to carry out our orders. It's not dishonorable to obey orders. I'm not so young as you think. Go on, tell me, in what war were you a spy?"

"It wasn't in any war," Aiken said, again turning away from me. "It was in Haskell's Private Detective Agency."

I could not prevent an exclamation, but the instant it had escaped me I could have kicked myself for having made it. "I beg your pardon," I murmured, awkwardly.

"I said you wouldn't understand," Aiken answered. Then, to show he did not wish to speak with me further, he spurred his mule into a trot and kept a distance between us.

Our trail ran over soft, spongy ground and was shut in on either hand by a wet jungle of tangled vines and creepers. They interlaced like the strands of a hammock, choking and strangling and clinging to each other in a great web. From the jungle we came to ill-smelling pools of mud and water, over which hung a white mist which rose as high as our heads. It was so heavy with moisture that our clothing dripped with it, and we were chilled until our teeth chattered. But by five o'clock in the morning we had escaped the coast swamps, and reached higher ground and the village of Sagua la Grande, and the sun was drying our clothes and taking the stiffness out of our bones.

CANAL COMPANY'S FEVER HOSPITAL,
PANAMA

The nurse brought me my diary this morning. She found it in the inside pocket of my tunic. All of its back pages were scribbled over with orders of the day, countersigns, and the memoranda I made after Laguerre appointed me adjutant to the Legion. But in the first half of it was what I see I was pleased to call my "memoirs," in which I had written the last chapter the day Aiken and I halted at Sagua la Grande. When I read it over I felt that I was somehow much older than when I made that last entry. And yet it was only two months ago. It seems like two years. I don't feel much like writing about it, nor thinking about it, but I suppose, if I mean to keep my "memoirs" up to date, I shall never have more leisure in which to write than I have now. For Dr. Ezequiel says it will be another two weeks before I can leave this cot. Sagua seems very unimportant now. But I must not write of it as I see it now, from this distance, but as it appealed to me then, when everything about me was new and strange and wonderful.

It was my first sight of a Honduranian town, and I thought it most charming and curious. As I learned later it was like any other Honduranian town and indeed like every other town in Central America. They are all built around a plaza, which sometimes is a park with fountains and tessellated marble pavements and electric lights, and sometimes only an open place of dusty grass. There is always a church at one end, and the café or club, and the alcalde's house, or the governor's palace, at another. In the richer plazas there must always be the statue of some Liberator, and in the poorer a great wooden cross. Sagua la Grande was bright and warm and foreign looking. It reminded me of the colored prints of Mexico which I had seen in my grandfather's library. The houses were thatched clay huts with gardens around them crowded with banana palms, and trees hung with long beans, which broke into masses of crimson flowers. The church opposite the inn was old and yellow, and at the edge of the plaza were great palms that rustled and courtesied. We led our mules straight through the one big room of the inn out into the yard behind it, and while doing it I committed the grave discourtesy of not first removing my spurs. Aiken told me about it at once, and I apologized to everyone—to the alcalde, and the priest, and the village school-master who had crossed the plaza to welcome us —and I asked them all to drink with me. I do not know that I ever enjoyed a breakfast more than I did the one we ate in the big cool inn with the striped awning outside, and the naked brown children watching us from the street, and the palms whispering overhead. The breakfast was good in itself, but it was my surroundings which made the meal so remarkable and the fact that I was no longer at home and responsible to someone, but that I was talking as one man to another, and in a foreign language to people who knew no other tongue. The inn-keeper was a fat little person in white drill and a red sash, in which he carried two silver-mounted pistols. He looked like a ring-master in a circus, but he cooked us a most won-derful omelette with tomatoes and onions and olives chopped up in it with oil. And an Indian woman made us tortillas, which are like our buck-wheat cakes. It was fascinating to see her toss them up in the air, and slap them into shape with her hands. Outside the sun blazed upon the white rim of huts, and the great wooden cross in the plaza threw its shadow upon the yellow façade of the church. Beside the church there was a chime of four bells swinging from a low ridge-pole. The dews and the sun had turned their copper a brilliant green, but had not hurt their music, and while we sat at breakfast a little Indian boy in crumpled vestments beat upon them with a stick, making a sweet and swinging melody. It did not seem to me a scene set for revolution, but I liked it all so much that that one breakfast alone repaid me for my long journey south. I was sure life in Sagua la Grande would always suit me, and that I would never ask for better company than the comic-opera landlord and the jolly young priest and the yellow-skinned, fever-ridden schoolmaster with his throat wrapped in a great woollen shawl. But very soon, what with having had no sleep the night before and the heat, I grew terribly drowsy and turned in on a canvas cot in the corner, where I slept until long after mid-day. For some time I could hear Aiken and the others conversing together and caught the names of Laguerre and Garcia, but I was too sleepy to try to listen, and, as I said, Sagua did not seem to me to be the place for conspiracies and revolutions. I left it with real regret, and as though I were parting with friends of long acquaintanceship.

From the time we left Sagua the path began to ascend, and we rode in single file along the edges of deep precipices. From the depths below giant ferns sent up cool, damp odors, and we could hear the splash and ripple of running water, and at times, by looking into the valley, I could see waterfalls and broad streams filled with rocks, which churned the water into a white foam. We passed under tall trees covered with white and purple flowers, and in the branches of others were perched macaws, giant parrots of the most wonderful red and blue and yellow, and just at sunset we startled hundreds of parroquets which flew screaming and chattering about our heads, like so many balls of colored worsted.

When the moon rose, we rode out upon a table-land and passed between thick forests of enormous trees, the like of which I had never imagined. Their branches began at a great distance from the ground and were covered thick with orchids, which I mistook for large birds roosting for the night. Each tree was bound to the next by vines like tangled ropes, some drawn as taut as the halyards of a ship, and others, as thick as one's leg; they were twisted and wrapped around the branches, so that they looked like boa-constrictors hanging ready to drop upon one's shoulders. The moonlight gave to this forest of

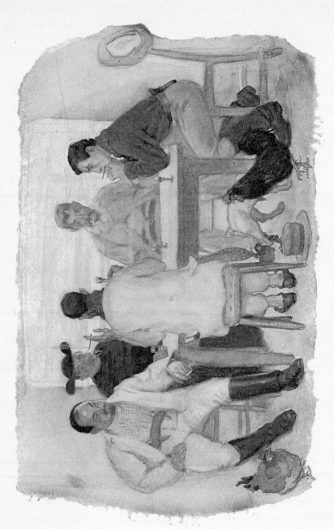

I was sure life in Sagua la Grande would always suit me.

before felt so far away from civilization and my own people. For company I made a little fire and sat before it, going over in my mind what I had learned since I had set forth on my travels. I concluded that so far I had gained much and lost much. What I had experienced of the ocean while on the ship and what little I had seen of this country delighted me entirely, and I would not have parted with a single one of my new impressions. But all I had learned of the cause for which I had come to fight disappointed and disheartened me. Of course I had left home partly to seek adventure, but not only for that. I had set out on this expedition with the idea that I was serving some good cause—that old-fashioned principles were forcing these men to fight for their independence. But I had been early undeceived. At the same time that I was enjoying my first sight of new and beautiful things I was being robbed of my illusions and my ideals. And nothing could make up to me for that. By merely travelling on around the globe I would always be sure to find some new things of interest. But what would that count if I lost my faith in men! If I ceased to believe in their unselfishness and honesty. Even though I were young and credulous, and lived in a make-believe world of my own imagining, I was happier so than in thinking that everyone worked for his own advantage, and without justice to others, or private honor. It harmed no one that I believed better of others than they deserved, but it was going to hurt me terribly if I learned that their aims were even lower than my own. I knew it was Aiken who had so discouraged me. It was he who had laughed at me for believing that Laguerre and his men were fighting for liberty. If I were going to credit him, there was not one honest man in Honduras, and no one on either side of this revolution was fighting for anything but money. He had made it all seem commercial, sordid, and underhand. I blamed him for having so shaken my faith and poisoned my mind. I scowled at his unconscious figure as he lay sleeping peacefully on his blanket, and I wished heartily that I had never set eyes on him. Then I argued that his word, after all, was not final. He made no pretence of being a saint, and it was not unnatural that a man who held no high motives should fail to credit them to others. I had partially consoled myself with this reflection, when I remembered suddenly that Beatrice herself had foretold the exact condition which Aiken had described.

"That is not war," she had said to me, "that is speculation!" She surely had said that to me, but how could she have known, or was hers only a random guess? And if she had guessed correctly what would she wish me to do now? Would she wish me to turn back, or, if my own motives were good, would she tell me to go on? She had called me her knight-errant, and I owed it to her to do nothing of which she would disapprove. As I thought of her I felt a great loneliness and a longing to see her once again. I thought of how greatly she would have delighted in those days at sea, and how wonderful it would have been if I could have seen this hot, feverish country with her at my side. I pictured her at the inn at Sagua smiling on the priest and the fat little landlord; and their admiration of her. I imagined us riding together in the brilliant sunshine with the crimson flowers meeting overhead, and the palms bowing to her and paying her homage. I lifted the locket she had wound around my wrist, and kissed it. As I did so, my doubts and questionings seemed to fall away. I stood up confident and determined. It was not my business to worry over the motives of other men, but to look to my own. I would go ahead and fight Alvarez, who Aiken himself declared was a thief and a tyrant. If anyone asked me my politics I would tell him I was for the side that would obtain the money the Isthmian Line had stolen, and give it to the people; that I was for Garcia and Liberty, Laguerre and the Foreign Legion. This platform of principles seemed to me so satisfactory that I stretched my feet to the fire and went to sleep.

I was awakened by the most delicious odor of coffee, and when I rolled out of my blanket I found José standing over me with a cup of it in his hand, and Aiken buckling the straps of my saddle-girth. We took a plunge in the stream, and after a breakfast of coffee and cold tortillas climbed into the saddle and again picked up the trail.

After riding for an hour Aiken warned me that at any moment we were likely to come upon either Laguerre or the soldiers of Alvarez. "So you keep your eyes and ears open," he said, "and when they challenge throw up your hands quick. The challenge is ' Halt, who lives,' " he explained. "If it is a government soldier you must answer, ' The government.' But if it's one of Laguerre's or Garcia's pickets you must say ' The revolution lives.' And whatever else you do, *hold up your hands.*"

I rehearsed this at once, challenging myself several times, and giving the appropriate answers. The performance seemed to afford Aiken much amusement.

"Isn't that right?" I asked.

"Yes," he said, "but the joke is that you won't be able to tell which is the government soldier and which is the revolutionist, and you'll give the wrong answer, and we'll both get shot."

"I can tell by our uniform," I answered.

"Uniform!" exclaimed Aiken, and burst into the most uproarious laughter. "Rags and tatters," he said.

I was considerably annoyed to learn by this that the revolutionary party had no distinctive uniform. The one worn by the government troops which I had seen at the coast I had thought bad enough, but it was a great disappointment to hear that we had none at all. Ever since I had started from Dobbs Ferry I had been wondering what was the Honduranian uniform. I had promised myself to have my photograph taken in it. I had anticipated the pride I should have in sending the picture back to Beatrice. So I was considerably chagrined, until I decided to invent a uniform of my own, which I would wear whether anyone else wore it or not. This was even better than having to accept one which someone else had selected. As I had thought much on the subject of uniforms, I began at once to design a becoming one.

We had reached a most difficult pass in the

mountain, where the trail stumbled over broken masses of rock and through a thick tangle of laurel. The walls of the pass were high and the trees at the top shut out the sunlight. It was damp and cold and dark.

"We're sure to strike something here," Aiken whispered over his shoulder. It did not seem at all unlikely. The place was the most excellent man-trap, but as to that, the whole length of the trail had lain through what nature had obviously arranged for a succession of ambushes.

Aiken turned in his saddle and said, in an anxious tone: "Do you know, the nearer I get to the old man, the more I think I was a fool to come. As long as I've got nothing but bad news, I'd better have stayed away. Do you remember Pharaoh and the messengers of ill tidings?"

I nodded, but I kept my eyes busy with the rocks and motionless laurel. My mule was slipping and kicking down pebbles, and making as much noise as a gun battery. I knew, if there were any pickets about, they could hear us coming for a quarter of a mile.

"Garcia may think he's Pharaoh," Aiken went on, "and take it into his head it's my fault the guns didn't come. Laguerre may say I sold the secret to the Isthmian Line."

"Oh, he couldn't think you'd do that!" I protested.

"Well, I've known it done," Aiken said. "Quay certainly sold us out at New Orleans. And Laguerre may think I went shares with him."

I began to wonder if Aiken was not probably the very worst person I could have selected to introduce me to General Laguerre. It seemed as though it certainly would have been better had I found my way to him alone. I grew so uneasy concerning my possible reception that I said, irritably: "Doesn't the General know you well enough to trust you?"

"No, he doesn't!" Aiken snapped back, quite as irritably. "And he's dead right, too. You take it from me, that the fewer people in this country you trust, the better for you. Why, the rottenness of this country is a proverb. 'It's a place where the birds have no song, where the flowers have no odor, where the women are without virtue, and the men without honor.' That's what a gringo said of Honduras many years ago, and he knew the country and the people in it."

It was not a comforting picture, but in my discouragement I remembered Laguerre.

"General Laguerre does not belong to this country," I said, hopefully.

"No," Aiken answered, with a laugh. "He's an Irish-Frenchman and belongs to a dozen countries. He's fought for every flag that floats, and he's no better off to-day than when he began."

He turned toward me and stared with an amused and tolerant grin. "He's a bit like you," he said.

I saw he did not consider what he said as a compliment, but I was vain enough to want to know what he did think of me, so I asked: "And in what way am I like General Laguerre?"

The idea of our similarity seemed to amuse Aiken, for he continued to grin.

"Oh, you'll see when we meet him," he said. "I can't explain it. You two are just different from other people—that's all. He's old-fashioned like you, if you know what I mean, and young——"

"Why, he's an old man," I corrected.

"He's old enough to be your grandfather," Aiken laughed, "but I say he's young—like you, the way you are."

Aiken knew that it annoyed me when he pretended I was so much younger than himself, and I had started on some angry reply, when I was abruptly interrupted.

A tall, ragged man rose suddenly from behind a rock, and presented a rifle. He was so close to Aiken that the rifle almost struck him in the face. Aiken threw up his hands, and fell back with such a jerk that he lost his balance, and would have fallen had he not pitched forward and clasped the mule around the neck. I pulled my mule to a halt, and held my hands as high as I could raise them. The man moved his rifle from side to side so as to cover each of us in turn, and cried in English, " Halt ! Who goes there ? "

Aiken had not told me the answer to that challenge, so I kept silent. I could hear José behind me interrupting his prayers with little sobs of fright.

Aiken scrambled back into an upright position, held up his hands, and cried : " Confound you, we are travellers, going to the capital on business. Who the devil are you ? "

" Qui vive ? " the man demanded over the barrel of his gun.

" What does that mean ? " Aiken cried, petulantly. " Talk English, can't you, and put down that gun."

The man ceased moving the rifle between us, and settled it on Aiken.

" Cry ' Long live the government,' " he commanded, sharply.

Aiken gave a sudden start of surprise, and I saw his eyelids drop and rise again. Later when I grew to know him intimately, I could always tell when he was lying, or making the winning move in some bit of knavery, by that nervous trick of the eyelids. He knew that I knew about it, and he once confided to me that, had he been able to overcome it, he would have saved himself some thousands of dollars which it had cost him at cards.

But except for this drooping of the eyelids he gave no sign.

"No, I won't cry 'Long live the government,'" he answered. "That is," he added hastily, "I won't cry long live anything. I'm the American Consul, and I'm up here on business. So's my friend."

The man did not move his gun by so much as a straw's breadth.

"You will cry 'Long live Alvarez' or I will shoot you," said the man.

I had more leisure to observe the man than had Aiken, for it is difficult to study the features of anyone when he is looking at you down a gun-barrel, and it seemed to me that the muscles of the man's mouth as he pressed it against the stock were twitching with a smile. As the side of his face toward me was the one farther from the gun, I was able to see this, but Aiken could not, and he answered, still more angrily: " I tell you, I'm the American Consul. Anyway, it's not going to do you any good to shoot me. You take me to your colonel alive, and I'll give you two hundred dollars. You shoot me and you won't get a cent."

The moment was serious enough, and I was thoroughly concerned both for Aiken and myself, but when he made this offer, my nervousness, or my sense of humor, got the upper hand of me, and I laughed.

Having laughed I made the best of it, and said:

"Offer him five hundred for the two of us. Hang the expense."

The rifle wavered in the man's hands, he steadied it, scowled at me, bit his lips, and then burst into shouts of laughter. He sank back against one of the rocks, and pointed at Aiken mockingly.

"I knew it was you all the time," he cried, "for certain I did. I knew it was you all the time."

I was greatly relieved, but naturally deeply indignant. I felt as though someone had jumped from behind a door, and shouted "Boo!" at me. I hoped in my heart that the colonel would give the fellow eight hours' pack drill. "What a remarkable sentry," I said.

Aiken shoved his hands into his breeches pockets, and surveyed the man with an expression of the most violent disgust.

"You've got a damned queer idea of a joke," he said finally. "I might have shot you!"

The man seemed to consider this the very acme of humor, for he fairly hooted at us. He was so much amused that it was some moments before he could control himself.

"I saw you at Porto Cortez," he said, "I knew you was the American Consul all the time. You came to our camp after the fight, and the General gave you a long talk in his tent. Don't you remember me? I was standing guard outside."

Aiken snorted indignantly.

"No, I don't remember you," he said. "But I'll remember you next time. Are you standing guard now, or just doing a little highway robbery on your own account?"

"Oh, I'm standing guard for keeps," said the sentry, earnestly. "Our camp's only two hundred yards back of me. And our Captain told me to let all parties pass except the enemy, but I thought I'd have to jump you just for fun. I'm an American myself, you see, from Kansas. An' being an American I had to give the American Consul a scare. But say," he exclaimed, advancing enthusiastically on Aiken, with his hand outstretched, " you didn't scare for a cent." He shook hands violently with each of us in turn. " My name's Pete MacGraw," he added, expectantly.

" Well, now, Mr. MacGraw," said Aiken, " if you'll kindly guide us to General Laguerre we'll use our influence to have you promoted. You need more room. I imagine a soldier with your original ideas must find sentry duty go very dull."

MacGraw grinned appreciatively and winked.

" If I take you to my General alive, do I get that two hundred dollars ? " he asked. He rounded off his question with another yell of laughter.

He was such a harmless idiot that we laughed with him. But we were silenced at once by a shout from above us, and a command to " Stop that noise." I looked up and saw a man in semi-uniform and wearing an officer's sash and sword stepping from one rock to another and breaking his way through the laurel. He greeted Aiken with a curt wave of the hand. " Glad to see you, Consul," he called. "You will dismount, please, and lead your horses this way." He looked at me suspiciously and then turned and disappeared into the undergrowth.

"The General is expecting you, Aiken," his voice called back to us. "I hope everything is all right?"

Aiken and I had started to draw the mules up the hill. Already both the officer and the trail had been completely hidden by the laurel.

"No, nothing is all right," Aiken growled.

There was the sound of an oath, the laurels parted, and the officer's face reappeared, glaring at us angrily.

"What do you mean?" he demanded.

"My information is for General Laguerre," Aiken answered, sulkily.

The man sprang away again muttering to himself, and we scrambled and stumbled after him, guided by the sounds of breaking branches and rolling stones.

From a glance I caught of Aiken's face I knew he was regretting now, with even more reason than before, that he had not remained at the coast, and I felt very sorry for him. Now that he was in trouble and not patronizing me and poking fun at me, I experienced a strong change of feeling toward him. He was the only friend I had in Honduras, and as between him and these strangers who had received us so oddly, I felt that, although it would be to my advantage to be friends with the greater number, my loyalty was owing to Aiken. So I scrambled up beside him and panted out with some difficulty, for the ascent was a steep one: "If there is any row, I'm with *you*, Aiken."

"Oh, there won't be any row," he growled.

"Well, if there is," I repeated, "you can count me in."

"That's all right," he said.

At that moment we reached the top of the incline, and I looked down into the hollow below. To my surprise I found that this side of the hill was quite barren of laurel or of any undergrowth, and that it sloped to a little open space carpeted with high, waving grass, and cut in half by a narrow stream. On one side of the stream a great herd of mules and horses were tethered, and on the side nearer us were many smoking camp-fires and rough shelters made from the branches of trees. Men were sleeping in the grass or sitting in the shade of the shelters, cleaning accoutrements, and some were washing clothes in the stream. At the foot of the hill was a tent, and ranged before it two Gatling guns strapped in their canvas jackets. I saw that I had at last reached my destination. This was the camp of the filibusters. These were the soldiers of Laguerre's Foreign Legion.

III

ALTHOUGH I had reached my journey's end, although I had accomplished what I had set out to do, I felt no sense of elation nor relief. I was, instead, disenchanted, discouraged, bitterly depressed. It was so unutterably and miserably unlike what I had hoped to find, what I believed I had the right to expect, that my disappointment and anger choked me. The picture I had carried in my mind was one of shining tent-walls, soldierly men in gay and gaudy uniforms, fluttering guidons, blue ammunition-boxes in orderly array, smart sentries pacing their posts, and a head-quarters tent where busy officers bent over maps and reports.

The scene I had set was one painted in martial colors, in scarlet and gold lace; it moved to martial music, to bugle-calls, to words of command, to the ringing challenge of the sentry, and what I had found was this camp of gypsies, this nest of tramps, without authority, discipline, or self-respect. It was not even picturesque. My indignation stirred me so intensely that, as I walked down the hill, I prayed for a rude reception, that I might try to express my disgust.

The officer who had first approached us stopped at the opening of the solitary tent, and began talking excitedly to someone inside. And as we reached the level ground, the occupant of the tent stepped from it. He was a stout, heavy man, with a long, twisted mustache, at which he was tugging fiercely. He wore a red sash and a bandman's tunic, with two stars sewn on the collar. I could not make out his rank, but his first words explained him.

"I am glad to see you at last, Mr. Aiken," he said. "I'm Major Reeder, in temporary command. You have come to report, sir?"

Aiken took so long to reply that I stopped studying the remarkable costume of the Major and turned to Aiken. I was surprised to see that he was unquestionably frightened. His eyes were shifting and blinking, and he wet his lips with his tongue. All his self-assurance had deserted him. The officer who had led us to the camp was also aware of Aiken's uneasiness, and was regarding him with a sneer. For some reason the spectacle of Aiken's distress seemed to afford him satisfaction.

"I should prefer to report to General Laguerre," Aiken said, at last.

"I am in command here," Reeder answered, sharply. "General Laguerre is absent—recon-

noitring. I represent him. I know all about
Mr. Quay's mission. It was I who recommended
him to the General. Where are the guns?"

For a moment Aiken stared at him helplessly,
and then drew in a quick breath.

"I don't know where they are," he said. "The
Panama arrived two days ago, but when I went
to unload the guns Captain Leeds told me they
had been seized in New Orleans by the Treasury
Department. Someone must have——"

Both Major Reeder and the officer interrupted
with a shout of anger.

"Then it's true!" Reeder cried. "It's true,
and—and—you dare to tell us so!"

Aiken raised his head and for a moment looked
almost defiant.

"Why shouldn't I tell you?" he demanded,
indignantly. "Who else was there to tell you?
I've travelled two days to let you know. I can't
help it if the news isn't good. I'm just as sorry
as you are."

The other officer was a stout, yellow-haired
German. He advanced a step and shook a soiled
finger in Aiken's face. "You can't help it, can't
you?" he cried. "You're sorry, are you? You
won't be sorry when you're paid your money,
will you? How much did you get for us, hey!
How much did Joe Fiske——"

Reeder threw out his arm and motioned the officer back. "Silence, Captain Heinze," he commanded.

The men of the Legion who had happened to be standing near the tent when we appeared had come up to look at the new arrivals, and when they heard two of their officers attacking Aiken they crowded still closer in front of us, forming a big half-circle. Each of them apparently was on a footing with his officers of perfect comradeship, and listened openly to what was going forward as though it were a personal concern of his own. They had even begun to discuss it among themselves, and made so much noise in doing so that Captain Heinze passed on Reeder's rebuke as though it had been intended for them, commanding, "Silence in the ranks."

They were not in ranks, and should not have been allowed where they were in any formation, but that did not seem to occur to either of the officers.

"Silence," Reeder repeated. "Now, Mr. Aiken, I am waiting. What have you to say?"

"What is there for me to say?" Aiken protested. "I have done all I could. I told you as soon as I could get here." Major Reeder drew close to Aiken and pointed his outstretched hand at him.

" Mr. Aiken," he said. " Only four people knew that those guns were ordered—Quay, who went to fetch them, General Laguerre, myself, and you. Some one of us must have sold out the others; no one else could have done it. It was not Quay. The General and I have been here in the mountains—we did not do it; and that—that leaves you."

" It does not leave me," Aiken cried. He shouted it out with such spirit that I wondered at him. It was the same sort of spirit which makes a rat fight because he can't get away, but I didn't think so then.

" It was Quay sold you out!" Aiken cried. " Quay told the Isthmian people as soon as the guns reached New Orleans. I suspected him when he cabled me he wasn't coming back. I know him. I know just what he is. He's been on both sides before."

" Silence, you—you," Reeder interrupted. He was white with anger. " Mr. Quay is my friend," he cried. " I trust him. I trust him as I would trust my own brother. How dare you accuse him !"

He ceased and stood gasping with indignation, but his show of anger encouraged Captain Heinze to make a fresh attack on Aiken.

" Quay took you off the beach," he shouted.

" He gave you food and clothes, and a bed to lie on. It's like you, to bite the hand that fed you. When have you ever stuck to any side or anybody if you could get a dollar more by selling him out?"

The whole thing had become intolerable. It was abject and degrading, like a falling-out among thieves. They reminded me of a group of drunken women I had once seen, shameless and foul-mouthed, fighting in the street, with grinning night-birds urging them on. I felt in some way horribly responsible, as though they had dragged me into it—as though the flying handfuls of mud had splattered me. And yet the thing which inflamed me the most against them was their unfairness to Aiken. They would not let him speak, and they would not see that they were so many, and that he was alone. I did not then know that he was telling the truth. Indeed, I thought otherwise. I did not then know that on those occasions when he appeared to the worst advantage, he generally was trying to tell the truth.

Captain Heinze pushed nearer, and shoved his fist close to Aiken's face.

"We know what you are," he jeered. " We know you're no more on our side than you're the American Consul. You lied to us about that, and you've lied to us about everything else. And now we've caught you, and we'll make you pay for it."

One of the men in the rear of the crowd shouted, "Ah, shoot the beggar!" and others began to push forward and to jeer. Aiken heard them and turned quite white.

"You've caught me?" Aiken stammered. "Why, I came here of my own will. Is it likely I'd have done that if I had sold you out?"

"I tell you you did sell us out," Heinze roared. "And you're a coward besides, and I tell you so to your face!" He sprang at Aiken, and Aiken shrank back. It made me sick to see him do it. I had such a contempt for the men against him that I hated his not standing up to them. It was to hide the fact that he had stepped back, that I jumped in front of him and pretended to restrain him. I tried to make it look as though had I not interfered, he would have struck at Heinze.

The German had swung around toward the men behind him, as though he were subpœnaing them as witnesses.

"I call him a coward to his face!" he shouted. But when he turned again I was standing in front of Aiken, and he halted in surprise, glaring at me. I don't know what made me do it, except that I had heard enough of their recriminations, and was sick with disappointment. I hated Heinze and all of them, and myself for being there.

"Yes, you can call him a coward," I said, as offensively as I could, "with fifty men behind you. How big a crowd do you want before you dare insult a man?" Then I turned on the others. "Aren't you ashamed of yourselves," I cried, "to all of you set on one man in your own camp? I don't know anything about this row and I don't want to know, but there's fifty men here against one, and I'm on the side of that one. You're a lot of cheap bullies," I cried, "and this German drill-sergeant," I shouted, pointing at Heinze, "who calls himself an officer, is the cheapest bully of the lot." I jerked open the buckle which held my belt and revolver, and flung them on the ground. Then I slipped off my coat, and shoved it back of me to Aiken, for I wanted to keep him out of it. It was the luck of Royal Macklin himself that led me to take off my coat instead of drawing my revolver. At the Point I had been accustomed to settle things with my fists, and it had been only since I started from the coast that I had carried a gun. A year later, in the same situation, I would have reached for it. Had I done so that morning, as a dozen of them assured me later, they would have shot me before I could have got my hand on it. But, as it was, when I rolled up my sleeves the men began to laugh, and some shouted: "Give him room," "Make a ring," "Fair play, now," "Make a ring." The semi-circle spread out and lengthened until it formed a ring, with Heinze and Reeder, and Aiken holding my coat, and myself in the centre of it.

I squared off in front of the German and tapped him lightly on the chest with the back of my hand.

"Now, then," I cried, taunting him, "I call *you* a coward to *your* face. What are you going to do about it?"

For an instant he seemed too enraged and astonished to move, and the next he exploded with a wonderful German oath and rushed at me, tugging at his sword. At the same moment the men gave a shout and the ring broke. I thought they had cried out in protest when they saw Heinze put his hand on his sword, but as they scattered and fell back I saw that they were looking neither at Heinze nor at me, but at someone behind me. Heinze, too, halted as suddenly as though he had been pulled back by a curbed bit, and, bringing his heels together, stood stiffly at salute. I turned and saw that everyone was falling out of the way of a tall man who came striding toward us, and I knew on the instant that he was General Laguerre. At the first glance I disassociated him from his followers. He was entirely apart. In any surroundings I would have picked him out as a leader of men. Even a civilian would have known he was a soldier, for the signs of his calling were stamped on him as plainly as the sterling mark on silver, and although he was not in uniform his carriage and countenance told you that he was a personage.

He was very tall and gaunt, with broad shoulders and a waist as small as a girl's, and although he must then have been about fifty years of age he stood as stiffly erect as though his spine had grown up into the back of his head.

At the first glance he reminded me of Van Dyke's portrait of Charles I. He had the same high-bred features, the same wistful eyes, and he wore his beard and mustache in what was called the Van Dyke fashion, before Louis Napoleon gave it a new vogue as the " imperial."

It must have been that I read the wistful look in his eyes later, for at the moment of our first meeting it was a very stern Charles I. who confronted us, with the delicate features stiffened in anger, and the eyes set and burning. Since then I have seen both the wistful look and the angry look many times, and even now I would rather face the muzzle of a gun than the eyes of General Laguerre when you have offended him.

Captain Macklin

His first words were addressed to Reeder.

"What does this mean, sir?" he demanded. "If you cannot keep order in this camp when my back is turned I shall find an officer who can. Who is this?" he added, pointing at me. I became suddenly conscious of the fact that I was without my hat or coat, and that my sleeves were pulled up to the shoulders. Aiken was just behind me, and as I turned to him for my coat I disclosed his presence to the General. He gave an exclamation of delight.

"Mr. Aiken!" he cried, "at last!" He lowered his voice to an eager whisper. "Where are the guns?" he asked.

Apparently Aiken felt more confidence in General Laguerre than in his officers, for at this second questioning he answered promptly.

"I regret to say, sir," he began, "that the guns were seized at New Orleans. Someone informed the Honduranian Consul there, and he——"

"Seized!" cried Laguerre. "By whom? Do you mean we have lost them?"

Aiken lowered his eyes and nodded.

"But how do you know?" Laguerre demanded, eagerly. "You are not sure? Who seized them?"

"The Treasury officers," Aiken answered.

"The captain of the Panama told me he saw the guns taken on the company's wharf."

For some moments Laguerre regarded him sternly, but I do not think he saw him. He turned and walked a few steps from us and back again. Then he gave an upward toss of his head as though he had accepted his sentence. "The fortunes of war," he kept repeating to himself, "the fortunes of war." He looked up and saw us regarding him with expressions of the deepest concern.

"I thought I had had my share of them," he said, simply. He straightened his shoulders and frowned, and then looked at us and tried to smile. But the bad news had cut deeply. During the few minutes since he had come pushing his way through the crowd, he seemed to have grown ten years older. He walked to the door of his tent and then halted and turned toward Reeder.

"I think my fever is coming on again," he said. "I believe I had better rest. Do not let them disturb me."

"Yes, General," Reeder answered. Then he pointed at Aiken and myself. "And what are we to do with these?" he asked.

"Do with these?" Laguerre repeated. "Why, what did you mean to do with them?"

Captain Macklin

Reeder swelled out his chest importantly. "If you had not arrived when you did, General," he said, "I would have had them shot!"

The General stopped at the entrance to the tent and leaned heavily against the pole. He raised his eyes and looked at us wearily and with no show of interest.

"Shoot them?" he asked. "Why were you going to shoot them?"

"Because, General," Reeder declared, theatrically, pointing an accusing finger at Aiken, "I believe this man sold our secret to the Isthmian Line. No one knew of the guns but our three selves and Quay. And Quay is not a man to betray his friends. I wish I could say as much for Mr. Aiken."

At that moment Aiken, being quite innocent, said even less for himself, and because he was innocent looked the trapped and convicted criminal.

Laguerre's eyes glowed like two branding-irons. As he fixed them on Aiken's face one expected to see them leave a mark.

"If the General will only listen," Aiken stammered. "If you will only give me a hearing, sir. Why should I come to your camp if I had sold you out? Why didn't I get away on the first steamer, and stay away—as Quay did?"

The General gave an exclamation of disgust, and shrugged his shoulders. He sank back slowly against one of the Gatling guns.

"What does it matter?" he said, bitterly. "Why lock the stable door now? I will give you a hearing," he said, turning to Aiken, "but it would be better for you if I listened to you later. Bring him to me to-morrow morning after roll-call. And the other?" he asked. He pointed at me, but his eyes, which were heavy with disappointment, were staring moodily at the ground.

Heinze interposed himself quickly.

"Aiken brought him here!" he said. "I believe he's an agent of the Isthmian people, or," he urged, "why did he come here? He came to spy out your camp, General, and to report on our condition."

"A spy!" said Laguerre, raising his head and regarding me sharply.

"Yes," Heinze declared, with conviction. "A spy, General. A Government spy, and he has found out our hiding-place and counted our men."

Aiken turned on him with a snarl.

"Oh, you ass!" he cried. "He came as a volunteer. He wanted to fight with you,—for the sacred cause of liberty!"

"Yes, he wanted to fight with us," shouted

Heinze, indignantly. "As soon as he got into the camp, he wanted to fight with us."

Laguerre made an exclamation of impatience, and rose unsteadily from the gun-carriage.

"Silence!" he commanded. "I tell you I cannot listen to you now. I will give these men a hearing after roll-call. In the meantime if they are spies, they have seen too much. Place them under guard; and if they try to escape, shoot them."

I gave a short laugh and turned to Aiken.

"That's the first intelligent military order I've heard yet," I said.

Aiken scowled at me fearfully, and Reeder and Heinze gasped. General Laguerre had caught the words, and turned his eyes on me. Like the real princess who could feel the crumpled rose-leaf under a dozen mattresses, I can feel it in my bones when I am in the presence of a real soldier. My spinal column stiffens, and my fingers twitch to be at my visor. In spite of their borrowed titles, I had smelt out the civilian in Reeder and had detected the non-commissioned man in Heinze, and just as surely I recognized the general officer in Laguerre.

So when he looked at me my heels clicked together, my arm bent to my hat and fell again to my trouser seam, and I stood at attention. It was as instinctive as though I were back at the Academy, and he had confronted me in the uniform and yellow sash of a major-general.

"And what do you know of military orders, sir," he demanded, in a low voice, "that you feel competent to pass upon mine?"

Still standing at attention, I said: "For the last three years I have been at West Point, sir, and have listened to nothing else."

"You have been at West Point?" he said, slowly, looking at me in surprise and with evident doubt. "When did you leave the Academy?"

"Two weeks ago," I answered. At this, he looked even more incredulous.

"How does it happen," he asked, "if you are preparing for the army at West Point, that you are now travelling in Honduras?"

"I was dismissed from the Academy two weeks ago," I answered. "This was the only place where there was any fighting, so I came here. I read that you had formed a Foreign Legion, and thought that maybe you would let me join it."

General Laguerre now stared at me in genuine amazement. In his interest in the supposed spy, he had forgotten the loss of his guns.

"You came from West Point," he repeated,

incredulously, "all the way to Honduras—to join me!" He turned to the two officers. "Did he tell you this?" he demanded.

They answered, "No," promptly, and truthfully as well, for they had not given me time to tell them anything.

"Have you any credentials, passports, or papers?" he said.

When he asked this I saw Reeder whisper eagerly to Heinze, and then walk away. He had gone to search my trunk for evidence that I was a spy, and had I suspected this I would have protested violently, but it did not occur to me then that he would do such a thing.

"I have only the passport I got from the commandanté at Porto Cortez," I said.

At the words Aiken gave a quick shake of the head, as a man does when he sees another move the wrong piece on the chess-board. But when I stared at him inquiringly his expression changed instantly to one of interrogation and complete unconcern.

"Ah!" exclaimed Heinze, triumphantly, "he has a permit from the Government."

"Let me see it," said the General.

I handed it to him, and he drew a camp-chair from the tent, and, seating himself, began to compare me with the passport.

" In this," he said at last, " you state that you are a commercial traveller ; that you are going to the capital on business, and that you are a friend of the Government."

I was going to tell him that until it had been handed me by Aiken, I had known nothing of the passport, but I considered that in some way this might involve Aiken, and so I answered :

" It was necessary to tell them any story, sir, in order to get into the interior. I could not tell them that I was *not* a friend of the Government, nor that I was trying to join you."

" Your stories are somewhat conflicting," said the General. " You are led to our hiding-place by a man who is himself under suspicion, and the only credentials you can show are from the enemy. Why should I believe you are what you say you are? Why should I believe you are not a spy ? "

I could not submit to having my word doubted, so I bowed stiffly and did not speak.

" Answer me," the General commanded, " what proofs have I ? "

" You have nothing but my word for it," I said.

General Laguerre seemed pleased with that, and I believe he was really interested in helping me to clear myself. But he had raised my temper by questioning my word.

" Surely you must have something to identify you," he urged.

" If I had I'd refuse to show it," I answered. " I told you why I came here. If you think I am a spy, you can go ahead and shoot me as a spy, and find out whether I told you the truth afterward."

The General smiled indulgently.

" There would be very little satisfaction in that for me, or for you," he said.

" I'm an officer and a gentleman," I protested, " and I have a right to be treated as one. If you serve every gentleman who volunteers to join you in the way I have been served, I'm not surprised that your force is composed of the sort you have around you."

The General raised his head and looked at me with such a savage expression that during the pause which ensued I was most uncomfortable.

" If your proofs you are an officer are no stronger than those you offer that you are a gentleman," he said, " perhaps you are wise not to show them. What right have you to claim you are an officer ? "

His words cut and mortified me deeply, chiefly because I felt I deserved them.

" Every cadet ranks a non - commissioned man," I answered.

"But you are no longer a cadet," he replied.
"You have been dismissed. You told me so
yourself. Were you dismissed honorably, or
dishonorably?"

"Dishonorably," I answered. I saw that this
was not the answer he had expected. He looked
both mortified and puzzled, and glanced at
Heinze and Aiken as though he wished that they
were out of hearing.

"What was it for—what was the cause of your
dismissal?" he asked. He now spoke in a much
lower tone. "Of course, you need not tell me,"
he added.

"I was dismissed for being outside the limits
of the Academy without a permit," I answered.
"I went to a dance at a hotel in uniform."

"Was that all?" he demanded, smiling.

"That was the crime for which I was dismissed," I said, sulkily. The General looked at
me for some moments, evidently in much doubt.
I believe he suspected that I had led him on to
asking me the reason for my dismissal, in order
that I could make so satisfactory an answer. As
he sat regarding me, Heinze bent over him and
said something to him in a low tone, to which
he replied: "But that would prove nothing. He
might have a most accurate knowledge of military
affairs, and still be an agent of the Government."

"That is so, General," Heinze answered, aloud. "But it would prove whether he is telling the truth about his having been at West Point. If his story is false in part, it is probably entirely false, as I believe it to be."

"Captain Heinze suggests that I allow him to test you with some questions," the General said, doubtfully; "questions on military matters. Would you answer them?"

I did not want them to see how eager I was to be put to such a test, so I tried to look as though I were frightened, and said, cautiously, "I will try, sir." I saw that the proposition to put me through an examination had filled Aiken with the greatest concern. To reassure him, I winked covertly.

Captain Heinze glanced about him as though looking for a text.

"Let us suppose," he said, importantly, "that you are an inspector-general come to inspect this camp. It is one that I myself selected; as adjutant it is under my direction. What would you report as to its position, its advantages and disadvantages?"

I did not have to look about me. Without moving from where I stood, I could see all that was necessary of that camp. But I first asked, timidly: "Is this camp a temporary one, made during a halt on the march, or has it been occupied for some days?"

"We have been here for two weeks," said Heinze.

"Is it supposed that a war is going on?" I asked, politely; "I mean, are we in the presence of an enemy?"

"Of course," answered Heinze. "Certainly we are at war."

"Then," I said, triumphantly, "in my report I should recommend that the officer who selected this camp should be court-martialled."

Heinze gave a shout of indignant laughter, and Aiken glared at me as though he thought I had flown suddenly mad, but Laguerre only frowned and waved his hand impatiently.

"You are bold, sir," he said, grimly; "I trust you can explain yourself."

I pointed from the basin in which we stood, to the thickly wooded hills around us.

"This camp has the advantage of water and grass," I said. I spoke formally, as though I were really making a report. "Those are its only advantages. Captain Heinze has pitched it in a hollow. In case of an attack, he has given the advantage of position to the enemy. Fifty men could conceal themselves on those ridges and fire upon you as effectively as though they had you

at the bottom of a well. There are no pickets
out, except along the trail, which is the one approach the enemy would not take. So far as this
position counts, then," I summed up, " the camp
is an invitation to a massacre."

I did not dare look at the General, but I pointed
at the guns at his side. " Your two field-pieces
are in their covers, and the covers are strapped on
them. It would take three minutes to get them
into action. Instead of being here in front of the
tent, they should be up there on those two highest points. There are no racks for the men's rifles
or ammunition belts. The rifles are lying on the
ground and scattered everywhere—in case of an
attack the men would not know where to lay their
hands on them. It takes only two forked sticks
and a ridge-pole with nicks in it, to make an excellent gun-rack, but there is none of any sort.
As for the sanitary arrangements of the camp, they
are *nil*. The refuse from the troop kitchen is
scattered all over the place, and so are the branches
on which the men have been lying. There is no
way for them to cross that stream without their
getting their feet wet; and every officer knows
that wet feet are worse than wet powder. The
place does not look as though it had been policed
since you came here. It's a fever swamp. If
you have been here two weeks, it's a wonder your

whole force isn't as rotten as sheep. And there!"
I cried, pointing at the stream which cut the camp
in two—"there are men bathing and washing their
clothes up-stream, and those men below them are
filling buckets with water for cooking and drinking.
Why have you no water-guards? You ought to
have a sentry there, and there. The water above
the first sentry should be reserved for drinking,
below him should be the place for watering your
horses, and below the second sentry would be the
water for washing clothes. Why, these things are
the A, B, C, of camp life." For the first time
since I had begun to speak, I turned on Heinze
and grinned at him.

"How do you like my report on your camp?"
I asked. "Now, don't you agree with me that
you should be court-martialled?" Heinze's
anger exploded like a shell.

"You should be court-martialled yourself!"
he shouted. "You are insulting our good General. For me, I do not care. But you shall not
reflect upon my commanding officer, for him
I——"

"That will do, Captain Heinze," Laguerre
said, quietly. "That will do, thank you." He
did not look up at either of us, but for some
time sat with his elbow on his knee and with his
chin resting in the palm of his hand, staring at

the camp. There was a long, and, for me, an awkward silence. The General turned his head and stared at me. His expression was exceedingly grave, but without resentment.

"You are quite right," he said, finally. Heinze and Aiken moved expectantly forward, anxious to hear him pass sentence upon me. Seeing this he raised his voice and repeated: "You are quite right in what you say about the camp. All you say is quite true."

He leaned forward with his elbows on his knees, and, as he continued speaking with his face averted, it was as though he were talking to himself.

"We grow careless as we grow older," he said. "One grows less difficult to please." His tone was that of a man excusing himself to himself. "The old standards, the old models, pass away and—and failures, failures come and dull the energy." His voice dropped into a monotone; he seemed to have forgotten us entirely.

It must have been then that for the first time I saw the wistful look come into his eyes, and suddenly felt deeply sorry for him and wished that I might dare to tell him so. I was not sorry for any act or speech of mine. They had attacked me, and I had only defended myself. I was not repentant for anything I had said; my sorrow was for what I read in the General's eyes as he sat staring out into the valley. It was the saddest and loneliest look that I had ever seen. There was no bitterness in it, but great sadness and weariness and disappointment, and above all, loneliness, utter and complete loneliness.

He glanced up and saw me watching him, and for a moment regarded me curiously, and then, as though I had tried to force my way into his solitude, turned his eyes quickly away.

I had forgotten that I was a suspected spy until the fact was recalled to me at that moment by the reappearance of Major Reeder. He came bustling past me, carrying as I saw, to my great indignation, the sword which had been presented to my grandfather, and which my grandfather had given to me. I sprang after him and twisted it out of his hand.

"How dare you!" I cried. "You have opened my trunk! How dare you pry into my affairs? General Laguerre!" I protested. "I appeal to you, sir."

"Major Reeder," the General demanded, sharply, "what does this mean?"

"I was merely seeking evidence, General," said Reeder. "You asked for his papers, and I went to look for them."

"I gave you no orders to pry into this gentleman's trunk," said the General. "You have exceeded your authority. You have done very ill, sir. You have done very ill."

While the General was reproving Reeder, his eyes, instead of looking at the officer, were fixed upon my sword. It was sufficiently magnificent to attract the attention of anyone, certainly of any soldier. The scabbard was of steel, wonderfully engraved, the hilt was of ivory, and the hilt-guard and belt fastenings were all of heavy gold. The General's face was filled with appreciation.

"You have a remarkably handsome sword there," he said, and hesitated, courteously, "—I beg your pardon, I have not heard your name?"

I was advancing to show the sword to him, when my eye fell upon the plate my grandfather had placed upon it, and which bore the inscription: "To Royal Macklin, on his appointment to the United States Military Academy, from his Grandfather, John M. Hamilton, Maj. Gen. U.S.A."

"My name is Macklin, sir," I said, "Royal Macklin." I laid the sword lengthwise in his hands, and then pointed at the inscription. "You will find it there," I said. The General bowed and bent his head over the inscription and then read the one beside it. This stated that the sword had been presented by the citizens of New York to Major-General John M. Hamilton in recognition of his distinguished services during the war with Mexico. The General glanced up at me in astonishment.

" General Hamilton ! " he exclaimed. " General John Hamilton ! Is that—was he your grandfather ? "

I bowed my head, and the General stared at me as though I had contradicted him.

" But, let me tell you, sir," he protested, " that he was my friend. General Hamilton was my friend for many years. Let me tell you, sir," he went on, excitedly, " that your grandfather was a brave and courteous gentleman, a true friend and—and a great soldier, sir, a great soldier. I knew your grandfather well. I knew him well." He rose suddenly, and, while still holding the sword close to him, shook my hand.

" Captain Heinze," he said, " bring out a chair for Mr. Macklin." He did not notice the look of injury with which Heinze obeyed this request. But I did, and I enjoyed the spectacle, and as Heinze handed me the camp-chair I thanked him politely. I could afford to be generous.

The General was drawing the sword a few inches from its scabbard and shoving it back again, turning it over in his hands.

" And to think that this is John Hamilton's sword," he said, " and that you are John Hamilton's grandson!" As the sword lay across his knees he kept stroking it and touching it as one might caress a child, glancing up at me from time to time with a smile. It seemed to have carried him back again into days and scenes to which we all were strangers, and we watched him without speaking. He became suddenly conscious of our silence, and, on looking up, seemed to become uncomfortably aware of the presence of Aiken and the two officers.

"That will do, gentlemen," he said. "You will return with Mr. Aiken after roll-call." The officers saluted as they moved away, with Aiken between them. He raised his eyebrows and tapped himself on the chest. I understood that he meant by this that I was to say a good word for him, and I nodded. When they had left us the General leaned forward and placed his hand upon my shoulder.

"Now tell me," he said. "Tell me everything. Tell me what you are doing here, and why you ran away from home. Trust me entirely, and do not be afraid to speak the whole truth."

I saw that he thought I had left home because I had been guilty of some wildness, if not of some crime, and I feared that my story would prove so inoffensive that he would think I was holding something back. But his manner was so gentle and generous that I plunged in boldly. I told him everything; of my life with my grandfather, of my disgrace at the Academy, of my desire, in spite of my first failure, to still make myself a soldier. And then I told him of how I had been disappointed and disillusioned, and how it had hurt me to find that this fight seemed so sordid and the motives of all engaged only mercenary and selfish. But once did he interrupt me, and then by an exclamation which I mistook for an exclamation of disbelief, and which I challenged quickly. "But it is true, sir," I said. "I joined the revolutionists for just that reason—because they were fighting for their liberty and because they had been wronged and were the under-dogs in the fight, and because Alvarez is a tyrant. I had no other motive. Indeed, you must believe me, sir," I protested, "or I cannot talk to you. It is the truth."

"The truth!" exclaimed Laguerre, fiercely; and as he raised his eyes I saw that they had suddenly filled with tears. "It is the first time I have heard the truth in many years. It is what I have preached myself for half a lifetime; what I have lived for and fought for. Why, here, now," he cried, "while I have been sitting listening to you, it was as though the boy I used to be had come back to talk to me, bringing my old ideals, the old enthusiasm." His manner and his tone suddenly altered, and he shook his head and placed his hand almost tenderly upon my own. "But I warn you," he said, " I warn you that you are wrong. You have begun young, and there is yet time for you to turn back; but if you hope for money, or place, or public favor, you have taken the wrong road. You will be a rolling-stone among milestones, and the way is all down hill. I began to fight when I was even younger than you. I fought for whichever party seemed to me to have the right on its side. Sometimes I have fought for rebels and patriots, sometimes for kings, sometimes for pretenders. I was out with Garibaldi, because I believed he would give a republic to Italy; but I fought against the republic of Mexico, because its people were rotten and corrupt, and I believed that the emperor would rule them honestly and well. I have always chosen my own side, the one which seemed to me promised the most good; and yet, after thirty years, I am where you see me to-night. I am an old man without a country, I belong to no political party, I have no family, I have no home. I have travelled over all the world looking for that country which was governed for the greater good of the greater number, and I have fought only for those men who promised to govern unselfishly and as the servants of the people. But when the fighting was over, and they were safe in power, they had no use for me nor my advice. They laughed, and called me a visionary and a dreamer. 'You are no statesman, General,' they would say to me. 'Your line is the fighting-line. Go back to it.' And yet, when I think of how the others have used their power, I believe that I could have ruled the people as well, and yet given them more freedom, and made more of them more happy."

The moon rose over the camp, and the night grew chill; but still we sat, he talking and I listening as I had used to listen when I sat at my grandfather's knee and he told me tales of war and warriors. They brought us coffee and food, and we ate with an ammunition-box for a table, he still talking and I eager to ask questions, and yet fearful of interrupting him. He told of great battles which had changed the history of Europe, of secret expeditions which had never been recorded even in his own diary, of revolutions which after months of preparation had burst forth and had been crushed between sunset and sunrise; of emperors, kings, patriots, and charlatans. There was nothing that I had wished to do, and that I had imagined myself doing, that he had not accomplished in reality—the acquaintances he had

The moon rose over the camp . . . but
still we sat.

success to be so envied as his failures. And in the glow and inspiration of his talk, and with the courage of a boy, I told him so. I think he was not ill pleased at what I said, nor with me. He seemed to approve of what I had related of myself, and of the comments I had made upon his reminiscences. He had said, again and again : "That is an intelligent question," "You have put your finger on the real weakness of the attack," "That was exactly the error in his strategy."

When he turned to enter his tent he shook my hand. "I do not know when I have talked so much," he laughed, "nor," he added, with grave courtesy, "when I have had so intelligent a listener. Good-night."

Throughout the evening he had been holding my sword, and as he entered the tent he handed it to me.

"Oh, I forgot," he said. "Here is your sword, Captain."

The flaps of the tent fell behind him, and I was left outside of them, incredulous and trembling.

I could not restrain myself, and I pushed the flaps aside.

"I beg your pardon, General," I stammered.

He had already thrown himself upon his cot, but he rose on his elbow and stared at me.

"What is it?" he demanded.

"I beg your pardon, sir," I gasped, "but what did you call me then—just now?"

"Call you," he said. "Oh, I called you 'captain.' You are a captain. I will assign you your troop to-morrow."

He turned and buried his face in his arm, and unable to thank him I stepped outside of the tent and stood looking up at the stars, with my grandfather's sword clasped close in my hands. And I was so proud and happy that I believe I almost prayed that he could look down and see me.

That was how I received my first commission —in a swamp in Honduras, from General Laguerre, of the Foreign Legion, as he lay half-asleep upon his cot. It may be, if I continue as I have begun, I shall receive higher titles, from ministers of war, from queens, presidents, and sultans. I shall have a trunk filled, like that of General Laguerre's, with commissions, brevets, and patents of nobility, picked up in many queer courts, in many queer corners of the globe.

But to myself I shall always be Captain Macklin, and no other rank nor title will ever count with me as did that first one, which came without my earning it, which fell from the lips of an old man without authority to give it, but which seemed to touch me like a benediction.

．　　．　　．　　．　　．　　．　　．

The officer from whom I took over my troop was a German, Baron Herbert von Ritter. He had served as an aide-de-camp to the King of Bavaria, and his face was a patchwork of sword-cuts which he had received in the students' duels. No one knew why he had left the German army. He had been in command of the troop with the rank of captain, but when the next morning Laguerre called him up and told him that I was now his captain he seemed rather relieved than otherwise.

"They're a hard lot," he said to me, as we left the General. "I'm glad to get rid of them."

The Legion was divided into four troops of about fifty men each. Only half of the men were mounted, but the difficulties of the trail were so great that the men on foot were able to move quite as rapidly as those on mule-back. Under Laguerre there were Major Webster, an old man, who as a boy had invaded Central America with William Walker's expedition, and who ever since had lived in Honduras; Major Reeder and five captains, Miller, who was in charge of a dozen native Indians and who acted as a scout; Captain Heinze, two Americans named Porter and Russell, and about a dozen lieutenants of every nationality.   Heinze had been adjutant of the force, but the morning after my arrival the General appointed me to that position, and at roll-call announced the change to the battalion.

"We have been waiting here for two weeks for a shipment of machine guns," he said to them. "They have not arrived and I cannot wait for them any longer.   The battalion will start at once for Santa Barbara, where I expect to get you by to-morrow night.   There we will join General Garcia, and continue with him until we enter the capital."

The men, who were properly weary of lying idle in the swamp, interrupted him with an enthusiastic cheer and continued shouting until he lifted his hand.

"Since we have been lying here," he said, "I have allowed you certain liberties, and discipline has relaxed.   But now that we are on the march again you will conduct yourselves like soldiers, and discipline will be as strictly enforced as in any army in Europe.   Since last night we have received an addition to our force in the person of Captain Macklin, who has volunteered his services.   Captain Macklin comes of a distinguished family of soldiers, and he has himself been educated at West Point.   I have appointed him Captain of D Troop and Adjutant of the Legion.

As adjutant you will recognize his authority as you would my own. You will now break camp, and be prepared to march in half an hour."

Soon after we had started we reached a clearing, and Laguerre halted us and formed the column into marching order. Captain Miller, who was thoroughly acquainted with the trail, and his natives, were sent on two hundred yards ahead of us as a point. They were followed by Heinze with his Gatling guns. Then came Laguerre and another troop, then Reeder with the two remaining troops and our "transport" between them. Our transport consisted of a dozen mules carrying bags of coffee, beans, and flour, our reserve ammunition, the General's tent, and whatever few private effects the officers possessed over and above the clothes they stood in. I brought up the rear with D Troop. We moved at a walk in single file and without flankers, as the jungle on either side of the trail was impenetrable. Our departure from camp had been so prompt that I had been given no time to become acquainted with my men, but as we tramped forward I rode along with them or drew to one side to watch them pass and took a good look at them. Carrying their rifles, and with their blanket-rolls and cartridge-belts slung across their shoulders, they made a better appearance

than when they were sleeping around the camp.
As the day grew on I became more and more
proud of my command. The baron pointed out
those of the men who could be relied upon, and
I could pick out for myself those who had received some military training. When I asked
these where they had served before, they seemed
pleased at my having distinguished the difference
between them and the other volunteers, and
saluted properly and answered briefly and re-
spectfully.

If I was proud of the men, I was just as
pleased with myself, or, I should say, with my
luck. Only two weeks before I had been read
out to the battalion at West Point, as one unfit
to hold a commission, and here I was riding at
the head of my own troop. I was no second
lieutenant either, with a servitude of five years
hanging over me before I could receive my first
bar, but a full-fledged captain, with fifty men
under him to care for and discipline and lead into
battle. There was not a man in my troop who
was not at least a few years older than myself,
and as I rode in advance of them and heard the
creak of the saddles and the jingle of the picket-
pins and water-bottles, or turned and saw the long
line stretching out behind me, I was as proud as
Napoleon returning in triumph to Paris. I had

brought with me from the Academy my scarlet
sash, and wore it around my waist under my
sword-belt. I also had my regulation gauntlets,
and a campaign sombrero, and as I rode along I
remembered the line about General Stonewall
Jackson, in " Barbara Frietchie,"

> The leader glancing left and right.

I repeated it to myself, and scowled up at the
trees and into the jungle. It was a tremendous
feeling to be a " leader."

At noon the heat was very great, and Laguerre halted the column at a little village and
ordered the men to eat their luncheon. I posted
pickets, appointed a detail to water the mules,
and asked two of the inhabitants for the use of
their clay ovens. In the other troops each man,
or each group of men, were building separate
fires and eating alone or in messes of five or six,
but by detailing four of my men to act as cooks
for the whole troop, and six others to tend the
fires in the ovens, and six more to carry water for
the coffee, all of my men were comfortably fed
before those in the other troops had their fires
going.

Von Ritter had said to me that during the two
weeks in camp the men had used up all their tobacco, and that their nerves were on edge for lack

of something to smoke. So I hunted up a native who owned a tobacco patch, and from him, for three dollars in silver, I bought three hundred cigars. I told Von Ritter to serve out six of them to each of the men of D Troop. It did me good to see how much they enjoyed them. For the next five minutes every man I met had a big cigar in his mouth, which he would remove with a grin, and say, " Thank you, Captain." I did not give them the tobacco to gain popularity, for in active service I consider that tobacco is as necessary for the man as food, and I also believe that any officer who tries to buy the good-will of his men is taking the quickest way to gain their contempt.

Soldiers know the difference between the officer who bribes and pets them, and the one who, before his own tent is set up, looks to his men and his horses, who distributes the unpleasant duties of the camp evenly, and who knows what he wants done the first time he gives an order, and does not make unnecessary work for others because he cannot make up his mind.

After I had seen the mules watered and picketed in the public corral, I went to look for the General, whom I found with the other officers at the house of the Alcalde. They had learned news of the greatest moment. Two nights previous, General Garcia had been attacked in force at Santa Barbara, and had abandoned the town without a fight. Nothing more was known, except that he was either falling back along the trail to join us, or was waiting outside the city for us to come up and join him.

Laguerre at once ordered the bugles to sound "Boots and saddles," and within five minutes we were on the trail again with instructions to press the men forward as rapidly as possible. The loss of Santa Barbara was a serious calamity. It was the town third in importance in Honduras, and it had been the stronghold of the revolutionists. The moral effect of the fact that Garcia held it, had been of the greatest possible benefit. As Garcia's force consisted of 2,000 men and six pieces of artillery, it was inexplicable to Laguerre how without a fight he had abandoned so valuable a position.

The country through which we now passed was virtually uninhabited, and wild and rough, but grandly beautiful. At no time, except when we passed through one of the dusty little villages, of a dozen sun-baked huts set around a sun-baked plaza, was the trail sufficiently wide to permit us to advance unless in single file. And yet this was the highway of Honduras from the Caribbean Sea to the Pacific Ocean, and the only road to Tegucigalpa, the objective point of our expedition. The capital lay only one hundred miles from Porto Cortez, but owing to the nature of this trail it could not be reached from the east coast, either on foot or by mule, in less than from six to nine days. No wheeled vehicle could have possibly attempted the trip without shaking to pieces, and it was only by dragging and lifting our Gatling guns by hand that we were able to bring them with us.

At sunset we halted at a little village, where, as usual, the people yelled " Vivas ! " at us, and protested that they were good revolutionists. The moon had just risen, and, as the men rode forward, kicking up the white dust and with the Gatlings clanking and rumbling behind them, they gave a most war-like impression. Miller, who had reconnoitred the village before we entered it, stood watching us as we came in. He said that we reminded him of troops of United States cavalry as he had seen them on the alkali plains of New Mexico and Arizona. It was again my duty to station our pickets and outposts, and as I came back after placing the sentries, the fires were twinkling all over the plaza and throwing grotesque shadows of the men and the mules against the white walls of the houses. It was a most weird and impressive picture.

Captain Macklin

The troopers were exhausted with the forced march, and fell instantly to sleep, but for a long time I sat outside the Town Hall talking with General Laguerre and two of the Americans, Miller and old man Webster. Their talk was about Aiken, who so far had accompanied us as an untried prisoner. From what he had said to me on the march, and from what I remembered of his manner when Captain Leeds informed him of the loss of the guns, I was convinced that he was innocent of any treachery.

I related to the others just what had occurred at the coast, and after some talk with Aiken himself, Laguerre finally agreed that he was innocent of any evil against him, and that Quay was the man who had sold the secret. Laguerre then offered Aiken his choice of continuing on with us, or of returning to the coast, and Aiken said that he would prefer to go on with our column. Now that the Isthmian Line knew that he had tried to assist Laguerre, his usefulness at the coast was at an end. He added frankly that his only other reason for staying with us was because he thought we were going to win. General Laguerre gave him charge of our transport and commissary, that is of our twelve pack-mules and of the disposition of the coffee, flour, and beans. Aiken possessed real executive ability, and it is only fair to him to say that as commissary sergeant he served us well. By the time we had reached Tegucigalpa the twelve mules had increased to twenty, and our stock of rations, instead of diminishing as we consumed them, increased daily. We never asked how he managed it. Possibly, knowing Aiken, it was wiser not to inquire.

We broke camp at four in the morning, but in spite of our early start the next day's advance was marked by the most cruel heat. We had left the shade of the high lands and now pushed on over a plain of dry, burning sand, where nothing grew but naked bushes bristling with thorns, and tall grayish-green cacti with disjointed branching arms. They stretched out before us against the blazing sky, like a succession of fantastic telegraph-poles. We were marching over what had once been the bed of a great lake. Layers of tiny round pebbles rolled under our feet, and the rocks which rose out of the sand had been worn and polished by the water until they were as smooth as the steps of a cathedral. A mile away on each flank were dark green ridges, but ahead of us there was only a great stretch of glaring white sand. No wind was stirring, and not a drop of moisture. The air was like a breath from a brick oven, and the heat of the sun so fierce that if you touched your fingers to a gun-barrel it burned the flesh.

We did not escape out of this lime-kiln until three in the afternoon, when the trail again led us into the protecting shade of the jungle. The men plunged into it as eagerly as though they were diving into water.

About four o'clock we heard great cheering ahead of us, and word was passed to the rear that Miller had come in touch with Garcia's scouts. A half hour later, we marched into the camp of the revolutionists. It was situated about three miles outside of Santa Barbara, on the banks of the river where the trail crossed it at a ford. Our fellows made a rather fine appearance as they rode out of the jungle among the revolutionists; and, considering the fact that we had come to fight for them, I thought the little beggars might have given us a cheer, but they only stared at us, and nodded stupidly. They were a mixed assortment, all of them under-size and either broad or swarthy, with the straight hair and wide cheek-bones of the Carib Indian, or slight and nervous looking, with the soft eyes and sharp profile of the Spaniard. The greater part of them had deserted in companies from the army, and they still wore the blue-jean uniform and carried the rifle and ac-coutrements of the Government. To distinguish themselves from those soldiers who had remained with Alvarez, they had torn off the red braid with which their tunics were embroidered.

All the officers of the Foreign Legion rode up the stream with Laguerre to meet General Garcia, whom we found sitting in the shade of his tent surrounded by his staff. He gave us a most enthusiastic greeting, embracing the General, and shaking hands with each of us in turn. He seemed to be in the highest state of excitement, and bustled about ordering us things to drink, and chattering, gesticulating, and laughing. He reminded me of a little, fat French poodle trying to express his delight by bounds and barks. They brought us out a great many bottles of rum and limes, and we all had a long, deep drink. After the fatigue and dust of the day, it was the best I ever tasted. Garcia's officers seemed just as much excited over nothing as he was, but were exceedingly friendly, treating us with an exaggerated " comrades-in-arms " and " brother-officers " sort of manner. The young man who entertained me was quite a swell, with a tortoise-shell visor to his cap and a Malacca sword-cane which swung from a gold cord. He was as much pleased over it as a boy with his first watch, and informed me that it had been used to assassinate his uncle, ex-President Rojas. As he seemed to consider it a very valuable heirloom, I moved my legs so that, as though by accident, my sword fell forward where he could see it. When he did he exclaimed upon its magnificence, and I showed him my name on the scabbard. He thought it had been presented to me for bravery. He was very much impressed.

Garcia and Laguerre talked together for a long time and then shook hands warmly, and we all saluted and returned to the ford.

As soon as we had reached it Laguerre seated himself under a tree and sent for all of his officers.

" We are to attack at daybreak to-morrow morning," he said. " Garcia is to return along the trail and make a demonstration on this side of the town, while we are here to attack from the other. The plaza is about three hundred yards from where we will enter. On the corner of the plaza and the main street there is a large warehouse. The warehouse looks across the plaza to the barracks, which are on the other side of the square. General Garcia's plan is that our objective point shall be this warehouse. It has two stories, and men on its roof will have a great advantage over those in the barracks and in the streets. He believes that when he begins his attack from this side, the Government troops will rush from the barracks and hasten toward the sound of the firing. At the same signal we are to hurry in from the opposite side of the town, seize the warehouse, and throw up barricades across the plaza. Should this plan succeed, the Government troops will find themselves shut in between two fires. It seems to be a good plan, and I have agreed to it. The cattle-path to the town is much too rough for our guns, so Captain Heinze and the gun detail will remain here and co-operate with General Garcia. Let your men get all the sleep they can now. They must march again at midnight. They will carry nothing but their guns and ammunition and rations for one meal. If everything goes as we expect, we will breakfast in Santa Barbara."

I like to remember the happiness I got out of the excitement of that moment. I lived at the rate of an hour a minute, and I was as upset from pure delight as though I had been in a funk of abject terror. And I was scared in a way, too, for whenever I remembered I knew nothing of actual fighting, and of what chances there were to make mistakes, I shivered down to my heels. But I would not let myself think of the chances to make a failure, but rather of the opportunities of doing something distinguished and of making myself conspicuous. I laughed when I thought

of my classmates at the Point with their eyes bent
on a book of tactics, while here was I, within
three hours of a real battle, of the most exciting
of all engagements, an attack upon a city. A full
year, perhaps many years, would pass before they
would get the chance to hear a hostile shot, the
shot fired in anger, which every soldier must first
hear before he can enter upon his inheritance, and
hold his own in the talk of the mess-table. I
felt almost sorry for them when I thought how
they would envy me when they read of the fight
in the newspapers. I decided it would be called
the battle of Santa Barbara, and I imagined how
it would look in the head-lines. I was even
generous enough to wish that three or four of the
cadets were with me; that is, of course, under
me, so that they could tell afterward how well I
had led them.

At midnight we filed silently out of camp, and
felt our way in the dark through the worst stretch
of country we had yet encountered. The ferns
rose above our hips, and the rocks and fallen logs
over which we stumbled were slippery with moss.
Every minute a man was thrown by a trailing
vine or would plunge over a fallen tree-trunk,
and there would be a yell of disgust and an oath
and a rattle of accoutrements. The men would
certainly have been lost if they had not kept in

touch by calling to one another, and the noise we made hissing at them for silence only added to the uproar.

At the end of three hours our guides informed us that for the last half-mile they had been guessing at the trail, and that they had now completely lost themselves. So Laguerre sent out Miller and the native scouts to buskey about and find out where we were, and almost immediately we heard the welcome barking of a dog, and one of the men returned to report that we had walked right into the town. We found that the first huts were not a hundred yards distant. Laguerre accordingly ordered the men to conceal themselves and sent Miller, one of Garcia's officers, and myself to reconnoitre.

The moonlight had given way to the faint gray light which comes just before dawn, and by it we could distinguish lumps of blackness which as we approached turned into the thatched huts of the villagers. Until we found the main trail into the town we kept close to the bamboo fences of these huts, and then, still keeping in the shadows, we followed the trail until it turned into a broad and well-paved street.

Except for many mongrel dogs that attacked us, and the roosters that began to challenge us from every garden, we had not been observed, and, so far as we could distinguish, the approach to the town was totally unprotected. By this time the light had increased sufficiently for us to see the white fronts of the houses, and the long empty street, where rows of oil-lamps were sputtering and flickering, and as they went out, filling the clean, morning air with the fumes of the dying wicks. It had been only two weeks since I had seen paved streets, and shops, and lamp-posts, but I had been sleeping long enough in the open to make the little town of Santa Barbara appear to me like a modern and well-appointed city. Viewed as I now saw it, our purpose to seize it appeared credulous and grotesque. I could not believe that we contemplated such a piece of folly. But the native officer pointed down the street toward a square building with overhanging balconies. In the morning mist the warehouse loomed up above its fellows of one story like an impregnable fortress.

Miller purred with satisfaction.

"That's the place," he whispered; "I remember it now. If we can get into it, they can never get us out." It seemed to me somewhat like burglary, but I nodded in assent, and we ran back through the outskirts to where Laguerre was awaiting us. We reported that there were no pickets guarding our side of the town, and the building Garcia had designated for defence seemed to us most admirably selected.

It was now near to the time set for the attack to begin, and Laguerre called the men together, and, as was his custom, explained to them what he was going to do. He ordered that when we reached the warehouse I was to spread out my men over the plaza and along the two streets on which the warehouse stood. Porter was to mount at once to the roof and open fire on the barracks, and the men of B and C Troops were to fortify the warehouse and erect the barricades.

It was still dark, but through the chinks of a few of the mud huts we could see the red glow of a fire, and were warned by this to move forward and take up our position at the head of the main street. Before we advanced, skirmishers were sent out to restrain any of the people in the huts who might attempt to arouse the garrison. But we need not have concerned ourselves, for those of the natives who came to their doors, yawning and shivering in the cool morning air, shrank back at the sight of us, and held up their hands. I suppose, as we crept out of the mist, we were a somewhat terrifying spectacle, but I know that I personally felt none of the pride of a conquering hero. The glimpse I had caught of the sleeping town, peaceful and unconscious, and the stealth and silence of our movements, depressed me greatly, and I was convinced that I had either perpetrated or was about to perpetrate some hideous crime. I had anticipated excitement and the joy of danger, instead of which, as I tiptoed between the poor gardens, I suffered all the quaking terrors of a chicken thief.

We had halted behind a long adobe wall to the right of the main street, and as we crouched there the sun rose like a great searchlight and pointed us out, and exposed us, and seemed to hold up each one of us to the derision of Santa Barbara. As the light flooded us we all ducked our heads simultaneously, and looked wildly about us as though seeking for some place to hide. I felt as though I had been caught in the open street in my night-gown. It was impossible to justify our presence. As I lay, straining my ears for Garcia's signal, I wondered what we would do if the worthy citizen who owned the garden wall, against which we lay huddled, should open the gate and ask us what we wanted. Could we reply that we, a hundred and fifty men, proposed to seize and occupy his city? I felt sure he would tell us to go away at once or he would call the police. I looked at the men near me, and saw that each was as disturbed as myself. A full quarter of an hour had passed since the time set for the attack, and still there was no signal from Garcia. The strain was becoming intolerable. At any moment some servant, rising earlier than his fellows, might stumble upon us, and in his surprise sound the alarm. Already in the trail behind us a number of natives, on their way to market, had been halted by our men, who were silently waving them back into the forest. The town was beginning to stir, wooden shutters banged against stone walls, and from but just around the corner of the main street came the clatter of iron bars as they fell from the door of a shop. We could hear the man who was taking them down whistling cheerily.

And then from the barracks came, sharply and clearly, the ringing notes of the reveille. I jumped to my feet and ran to where Laguerre was sitting with his back to the wall.

" General, can't I begin now? " I begged. " You said D Troop was to go in first."

He shook his head impatiently. " Listen ! " he commanded.

We heard a single report, but so faintly and from such a distance that had it not instantly been followed by two more we could not have distinguished it. Even then we were not certain. Then as we crouched listening, each reading the face of the others and no one venturing to breathe, there came the sharp, broken roll of musketry. It was unmistakable. The men gave a great gasp of relief, and without orders sprang to "attention." A ripple of rifle-fire, wild and scattered, answered the first volley.

"They have engaged the pickets," said Laguerre.

The volleys were followed by others, and volleys, more uneven, answered them still more wildly.

"They are driving the pickets back," explained Laguerre. We all stood looking at him as though he were describing something which he actually saw. Suddenly from the barracks came the discordant calls of many bugles, warning, commanding, beseeching.

Laguerre tossed back his head, like a horse that has been too tightly curbed.

"They are leaving the barracks," he said. He pulled out his watch and stood looking down at it in his hand.

"I will give them three minutes to get under way," he said. "Then we will start for the warehouse. When they come back again, they will find us waiting for them."

It seemed an hour that we stood there, and during every second of that hour the rifle-fire increased in fierceness and came nearer, and seemed to make another instant of inaction a crime. The men were listening with their mouths wide apart, their heads cocked on one side, and their eyes staring. They tightened their cartridge-belts nervously, and opened and shot back the breech-bolts of their rifles. I took out my revolver, and spun the cylinder to reassure myself for the hundredth time that it was ready. But Laguerre stood quite motionless, with his eyes fixed impassively upon his watch as though he were a physician at a sick-bed. Only once did he raise his eyes. It was when the human savageness of the rifle-fire was broken by a low mechanical rattle, like the whirr of a mowing-machine as one hears it across the hay-fields. It spanked the air with sharp hot reports.

"Heinze has turned the Gatlings on them," he said. "They will be coming back soon." He closed the lid of his watch with a click and nodded gravely at me. "You can go ahead now, Captain," he said. His tone was the same as though he had asked me to announce dinner.

IV

I JUMPED toward the street at the double, and the men followed me crowded in a bunch. I shouted back at them to spread out, and they fell apart. As I turned into the street I heard a shout from the plaza end of it and found a dozen soldiers running forward to meet us. When they saw the troops swing around the corner, they halted and some took cover in the doorways, and others dropped on one knee in the open street, and fired carefully. I heard soft, whispering sounds stealing by my head with incredible slowness, and I knew that at last I was under fire. I no longer felt like a boy robbing an orchard, nor a burglar. I was instead grandly excited and happy, and yet I was quite calm too. I am sure of this, for I remember I calculated the distance between us and the warehouse, and compared it with the two hundred and twenty-yard stretch in an athletic park at home. As I ran I noted also everything on either side of me: two girls standing behind the iron bars of a window with their hands pressed to their cheeks, and a negro with a broom in his hand crouching in a doorway. Some of the men stopped running and halted to fire, but I shouted to them to come on. I was sure if we continued to charge we could frighten off the men at the end of the street, and I guessed rightly, for as we kept on they scattered and ran. I could hear shouts and screams rising from many different houses, and men and women scuttled from one side of the street to the other like frightened hens.

As we passed an open shop some men inside opened a fusillade on me, and over my shoulder I just caught a glimpse of one of them as he dropped back behind the counter. I shouted to Von Ritter, who was racing with me, to look after them, and saw him and a half-dozen others swerve suddenly and sweep into the shop. Porter's men were just behind mine and the noise our boots made pounding on the cobblestones sounded like a stampede of cattle.

The plaza was an unshaded square of dusty grass. In the centre was a circular fountain, choked with dirt and dead leaves, and down the paths which led to it were solid stone benches. I told the men to take cover inside the fountain, and about a dozen of them dropped behind the rim of it, facing toward the barracks. I heard Porter give a loud "hurrah!" at finding the doors of the warehouse open, and it seemed al-

..10st instantly that the men of his troop began to fire over our heads from its roof. At the first glance it was difficult to tell from where the enemy's fire came, but I soon saw smoke floating from the cupola of the church on the corner and drifting through the barred windows of the barracks. I shouted at the men behind the benches to aim at the cupola, and directed those with me around the fountain to let loose at the barrack windows. As they rose to fire and exposed themselves above the rim of the fountain three of them were hit, and fell back swearing. The men behind the benches shouted at me to take cover, and one of the wounded men in the fountain reached up and pulled at my tunic, telling me to lie down. The men of B and C Troops were rolling casks out of the warehouse and building a barricade, and I saw that we were drawing all of the fire from them. We were now in a cross-fire between the church and the barracks, and were getting very much the worst of the fight. The men in the barracks were only seventy yards away. They seemed to be the ones chiefly responsible. They had piled canvas cots against the bars of the windows, and though these afforded them no protection, they prevented our seeing anything at which to shoot.

One of my men gave a grunt, and whirled

over, holding his hand to his shoulder. "I've got it, Captain," he said. I heard another man shriek from behind one of the benches. Our position was becoming impossible. It was true we were drawing the fire from the men who were working on the barricade, which was what we had been sent out to do, but in three minutes I had lost five men.

I remembered a professor at the Point telling us the proportion of bullets that went home was one to every three hundred, and I wished I had him behind that fountain. Miller was lying at my feet pumping away with a Winchester. As he was reloading it he looked up at me, and shouted, "And they say these Central Americans can't shoot!" I saw white figures appearing and disappearing at the windows of almost every house on the plaza. The entire population seemed to have taken up arms against us. The bullets splashed on the combing of the fountain and tore up the grass at our feet, and whistled and whispered about our ears. It seemed utter idiocy to remain, but I could not bring myself to run back to the barricade.

In the confusion which had ensued in the barracks when Garcia opened the attack the men who ran out to meet him had left the gates of the barrack yard open, and as I stood, uncertain what to

like children. We tore the cots away from the
windows and waved at the men behind the barricade, and they stood up and cheered us, and the
men on the roof, looking very tall against the
blue sky, stood up and waved their hats and
cheered too. They had silenced the men in the
cupola, and a sudden hush fell upon the plaza.
It was easy to see that many sympathizers with
the government had been shooting at us from the
private houses. When they saw us take the barracks they had probably decided that the time
had come to wipe off the powder-stains, and reap-
pear as friends of the revolution. The only firing
now was from where Garcia was engaged. Judg-
ing from the loudness of these volleys he had
reached the outskirts of the town. I set half of
my force to work piling up bags of meal behind
the iron bars, and, in the event of fire, filling pails
with water, and breaking what little glass still remained in the windows. Others I sent to bring
in the wounded, and still others to serving out
the coffee and soup we had found in the kitchen.
After giving these orders I ran to the barricade
to report. When I reached it the men behind it
began to rap on the stones with the butts of their
rifles as people pound with their billiard-cues
when someone has made a difficult shot, and
those on the roof leaned over and clapped their

hands. It was most unmilitary, but I must say I was pleased by it, though I pretended I did not know what they meant.

Laguerre came to the door of the warehouse, and smiled at me.

"I'm glad you're still alive, sir," he said. "After this, when you get within seventy yards of the enemy, I hope you will be able to see him without standing up."

The men above us laughed, and I felt rather foolish, and muttered something about "setting an example."

"If you get yourself shot," he said, "you will be setting a very bad example, indeed. We can't spare anybody, Captain, and certainly not you." I tried to look as modest as possible, but I could not refrain from glancing around to see if the men had heard him, and I observed with satisfaction that they had.

Laguerre asked me if I could hold the barracks, and I told him that I thought I could. He then ordered me to remain there.

"Would you like a cup of coffee, General?" I asked. The General's expression changed swiftly. It became that of a very human and a very hungry man.

"Have you got any?" he demanded anxiously.

"If you can lend me some men," I said, " I

can send you back eight gallons." At this the men behind the barricades gave a great cheer of delight, and the General smiled and patted me on the shoulder.

"That is right," he said. "The best kind of courage often comes from a full stomach. Run along now," he added, as though he were talking to a child, "run along, and don't fire until we do, and send us that coffee before we get to work again."

I called in all of my men from the side streets, and led them across to the barracks. I placed some of them on the roof and some of them on tables set against the inside of the wall in the yard.

As I did so, I saw Porter run across the plaza with about fifty of his men, and almost immediately after they had disappeared we heard cheering, and he returned with Captain Heinze. They both ran toward General Laguerre, and Porter then came across to me, and told me that the government troops were in full flight, and escaping down the side streets into the jungle. They were panic-stricken and were scattering in every direction, each man looking after his own safety. For the next two hours I chased terrified little soldiers all over the side of the town which had been assigned me, either losing them at the edge of the jungle, or dragging them out of shops and private houses. No one was hurt. It was only necessary to fire a shot after them to see them throw up their hands. By nine o'clock I had cleaned up my side of the town, and returned to the plaza. It was now so choked with men and mules that I was five minutes in forcing my way across. Garcia's troops had marched in, and were raising a great hullabaloo, cheering and shouting, and embracing the townspeople, whom they had known during their former occupation, and many of whom were the same people who had been firing at us. I found Laguerre in counsel with Garcia, who was in high spirits, and feeling exceedingly pleased with himself. He entirely ignored our part in taking the town, and talked as though he had captured it single-handed. The fact that the government troops had held him back until we threatened them in the rear he did not consider as important. I resented his swagger and the way he patronized Laguerre, but the General did not seem to notice it, or was too well satisfied with the day's work to care. While I was at head-quarters our scouts came in to report that the enemy was escaping along the trail to Comyagua, and that two of their guns had stalled in the mud, not one mile out from Santa Barbara. This was great news, and to my delight I was among those who hurried out to the place where the guns were supposed to be. We found them abandoned and stuck in the mud, and captured them without firing a shot. A half hour later we paraded our prizes in a triumphal procession through the streets of Santa Barbara, and were given a grand welcome by the allies and the townspeople. I had never witnessed such enthusiasm, but it was not long before I found out the cause of it. In our absence everybody had been celebrating the victory with aguardiente, and half of Garcia's warriors had become so hopelessly drunk that they were lying all over the plaza, and their comrades were dancing and tramping upon them.

I found that this orgy had put Laguerre in a fine rage, and I heard him send out the provost guard with orders to throw all the drunken men into the public corral for lost mules.

When he learned of this Garcia was equally indignant. The matter ended with Laguerre's locking up Garcia's soldiers with our prisoners-of-war in the yard barracks, where they sang and shouted and fought until they were exhausted and went to sleep.

There was still much drink left on requisition, but the conquering heroes had taken everything there was to eat, and for some time I wandered around seeking for food before I finally discovered Miller, Von Ritter, and Aiken in the garden of a private house enjoying a most magnificent luncheon. I begged a share on the ground that I had just overcome two helpless brass cannon, and they gave me a noisy welcome, and made a place for me. I was just as happy as I was hungry, and I was delighted to find someone with whom I could discuss the fight. For an hour we sat laughing and drinking, and each talking at the top of his voice and all at the same time. We were as elated as though we had captured the city of London.

Of course Aiken had taken no part in the fight, and of course he made light of it, which was just the sort of thing he would do, and he especially poked fun at me and at my charge on the barracks. He called it a " grand-stand play," and said I was a " gallery fighter." He said the reason I ran out into the centre of the plaza was because I knew there was a number of women looking out of the windows, and he pretended to believe that when we entered the barracks they were empty, and that I knew they were when I ordered the charge.

" It was the coffee they were after," he declared. " As soon as Macklin smelt the coffee he drew his big gilt sword and cried, ' Up, my men,

174

inside yon fortress a free breakfast awaits us. Follow your gallant leader!' and they never stopped following until they reached the kitchen. They're going to make Macklin a bugler," he said, " so that after this he can blow his own trumpet without anyone being allowed to interrupt him."

I was glad to find that I could take what Aiken said of me as lightly as did the others. Since the fight his power to annoy me had passed. I knew better than anyone else that at one time during the morning I had been in a very tight place, but I had stuck to it and won out The knowledge that I had done so gave me confidence in myself—not that I have ever greatly lacked it, but it was a new kind of confidence. It made me feel older, and less inclined to boast. In this it also helped out my favorite theory that it must be easy for the man who has done something to be modest. After he has proved himself capable in the eyes of his comrades he doesn't have to go about telling them how good he is. It is a saying that heroes are always modest, but they are not really modest. They just keep quiet, because they know their deeds are better talkers than they are.

Miller and I had despatched an orderly to inform Laguerre of our whereabouts, and at three o'clock in the afternoon the man returned to tell us that we were to join the General in the plaza. On arriving there we found the column already drawn up in the order of march, and an hour later we filed out of the town down the same street by which we had entered it that morning, and were cheered by the same people who eight hours before had been firing upon us. We left five hundred of Garcia's men to garrison the place and prevent the townspeople from again changing their sympathies, and continued on toward Tegucigalpa with Garcia and the remainder of his force as our main body, and with the Legion in the van. We were a week in reaching Comyagua, which was the only place that we expected would offer any resistance until we arrived outside of the capital. During that week our march was exactly similar to the one we had made from the camp to Santa Barbara. There was the same rough trail, the jungle crowding close on either flank, the same dusty villages, the same fierce heat. At the villages of Tabla Ve and at Segua-atepec our scouts surprised the rear guard of the enemy and stampeded it without much difficulty, and with only twenty men wounded. As usual we had no one to thank for our success in these skirmishes but ourselves, as Garcia's men never appeared until just as the fight was over, when they would come running up in great excitement. Laguerre remarked that they needed a better knowledge of the bugle calls, as they evidently mistook our " Cease firing " for " Advance."

The best part of that week's march lay in the many opportunities it gave me to become acquainted with my General. The more I was permitted to be with him the longer I wanted to be always with him, and with no one else. After listening to Laguerre you felt that a talk with the other men was a waste of time. There was nothing apparently that he did not know of men and events, and his knowledge did not come from books, but at first hand, from contact with the men, and from having taken part in the events.

After we had pitched camp for the night the others would elect me to go to his tent, and ask if we could come over and pay our respects. They always selected me for this errand, because they said it was easy to see that I was his favorite.

When we were seated about him on the rocks, or on ammunition boxes, or on the ground, I would say, " Please, General, we want to hear some stories," and he would smile and ask, " What sort of stories ? " and each of us would ask for something different. Some would want to hear about the Franco-Prussian war, and others of the Fall of Plevna or Don Carlos or Garibaldi, or of the Confederate generals with whom Laguerre had fought in Egypt.

When the others had said good-night he would sometimes call me back on the pretence of giving me instructions for the morrow, and then would come the really wonderful stories—the stories that no historian has ever told. His talk was more educational than a library of histories, and it filled me with a desire to mix with great people —to be their companion as he had been, to have kings and pretenders for my intimates. When one listened it sounded easy of accomplishment. It never seemed strange to him that great rulers should have made a friend of a stray soldier of fortune, an Irish adventurer—for Laguerre's mother was Irish; his father had been Colonel Laguerre, and once Military Governor of Algiers—and given him their confidence. And yet I could see why they should do so, for just the very reason that he took their confidence as a matter of course, knowing that his loyalty would always be above suspicion. He had a great capacity for loyalty. There was no taint in it of self-interest, nor of snobbishness. He believed, for instance, in the divine right of kings; and from what he let fall we could see that he had given the most remarkable devotion not only to every cause for which he had fought, but to the individual who represented it. That in time each of these individuals had disappointed him had in no way shaken his faith in the one to whom he next offered his sword. His was a most beautiful example of modesty and of faith in one's fellowman. It was during this week, and because of these midnight talks with him around the campfire, that I came to look up to him, and love him like a son.

But during that same week I was annoyed to find that many of our men believed the version which Aiken had given of my conduct at Santa Barbara. There were all sorts of stories circulating through the Legion about me. They made me out a braggart, a bully, and a conceited ass—indeed, almost everything unpleasant was said of me except that I was a coward. Aiken, of course, kindly retold these stories to me, either with the preface that he thought I ought to know what was being said of me, or that he thought the stories would amuse me. I thanked him and pretended to laugh, but I felt more like punching his head. People who say that women are gossips, and that they delight in tearing each other to pieces, ought to hear the talk of big, broad-shouldered men around camp-fires. If you believe what they

say, you would think that every officer had either
bungled or had funked the fight. And when a
man really has performed some act which cannot
be denied they call him a " swipe," and say he
did it to gain promotion, or to curry favor with
the General. Of course, it may be different in
armies officered by gentlemen; but men are
pretty much alike all the world over, and I know
that those in our Legion were as given to gossip
and slander as the inmates of any Old Woman's
Home. I used to say to myself that so long as
I had the approval of Laguerre and of my own
men and of my conscience I could afford not to
mind what the little souls said ; but as a matter
of fact I did mind it, and it angered me exceedingly. Just as it hurt me at the Point to see
that I was not popular, it distressed me to find
that the same unpopularity had followed me into
the Legion. The truth is that the officers were
jealous of me. They envied me my place as
Adjutant, and they were angry because Laguerre assigned one so much younger than
themselves to all the most important duties.
They said that by showing favoritism he was
weakening his influence with the men and that he
made a " pet " of me. If he did I know that he
also worked me five times as hard as anyone else,
and that he sent me into places where no one but

himself would go. The other officers had really no reason to object to me personally. I gave them very little of my company, and though I spoke pleasantly when we met I did not associate with them. Miller and Von Ritter were always abusing me for not trying to make friends; but I told them that, since the other officers spoke of me behind my back as a cad, braggart, and snob, the least I could do was to keep out of their way.

I was even more unpopular with the men, but there was a reason for that; for I was rather severe with them, and imposed as strict a discipline on them as that to which I had been accustomed at West Point. The greater part of them were ne'er-do-wells and adventurers picked up off the beach at Greytown, and they were a thoroughly independent lot, reckless and courageous; but I doubt if they had ever known authority or restraint, unless it was the restraint of a jail. With the men of my own troop I got on well enough, for they saw I understood how to take care of them, and that things went on more smoothly when they were carried out as I had directed, so they obeyed me without sulking. But with the men of the troops not directly under my command I frequently met with trouble; and on several occasions different men refused to obey my orders as Adjutant, and swore and even struck at me, so that I had to knock them down. I regretted this exceedingly, but I was forced to support my authority in some way. After learning the circumstances Laguerre exonerated me, and punished the men. Naturally, this did not help me with the volunteers, and for the first ten days after I had joined the Legion I was the most generally disliked man in it. This lasted until we reached Comyagua, when something happened which brought the men over to my side. Indeed, I believe I became a sort of a hero with them, and was nearly as popular as Laguerre himself. So in the end it came out all right, but it was near to being the death of me ; and, next to hanging, the meanest kind of a death a man could suffer.

When this incident occurred, which came so near to ending tragically for me, we had been trying to drive the government troops out of the cathedral of Comyagua. It was really a church and not a cathedral, but it was so much larger than any other building we had seen in Honduras that the men called it " The Cathedral." It occupied one whole side of the plaza. There were four open towers at each corner, and the front entrance was as large as a barn. Their cannon, behind a barricade of paving stones, were on the steps which led to this door.

Captain Macklin

I carried a message from Laguerre along the end of the plaza opposite the cathedral, and as I was returning, the fire grew so hot that I dropped on my face. There was a wooden watering-trough at the edge of the sidewalk, and I crawled over and lay behind it. Directly back of me was a restaurant into which a lot of Heinze's men had broken their way from the rear. They were firing up at the men in the towers of the cathedral. My position was not a pleasant one, for every time I raised my head the soldiers in the belfry would cut loose at me; and, though they failed to hit me, I did not dare to get up and run. Already the trough was leaking like a sieve. There was no officer with the men in the café, so they were taking the word from one of their own number, and were firing regularly in volleys. They fired three times after I took shelter. They were so near me that at each volley I could hear the sweep of the bullets passing about two yards above my head.

But at the fourth volley a bullet just grazed my cheek and drove itself into the wood of the trough. It was so near that the splinters flew in my eyes. I looked back over my shoulder and shouted, " Look out! You nearly hit me then. Fire higher."

One of the men in the café called back, " We can't hear you," and I repeated, " Fire higher !

You nearly hit me," and pointed with my finger to where the big 44-calibre ball had left a black hole in the green paint of the trough. When they saw this there were excited exclamations from the men, and I heard the one who was giving the orders repeating my warning. And then came the shock of another volley. Simultaneously with the shock a bullet cut through the wide brim of my sombrero and passed into the box about two inches below my chin.

It was only then that I understood that this was no accident, but that someone in the restaurant was trying to murder me. The thought was hideous and sickening. I could bear the fire of the enemy from the belfry—that was part of the day's work; the danger of it only excited me; but the idea that one of my own side was lying within twenty feet of me, deliberately aiming with intent to kill, was outrageous and revolting.

I scrambled to my feet and faced the open front of the restaurant, and as I stood up there was, on the instant, a sharp fusillade from the belfry tower. But I was now far too angry to consider that. The men were kneeling just inside the restaurant, and as I halted a few feet from them I stuck my finger through the bullet hole and held up my hat for them to see.

" Look ! " I shouted at them. " You did that,

you cowards. You want to murder me, do you? "
I straightened myself and threw out my arms,
" Well, here's your chance," I cried. " Don't
shoot me in the back. Shoot me now."

The men gaped at me in utter amazement.
Their lips hung apart. Their faces were drawn in
lines of anger, confusion, and dislike.

" Go on!" I shouted. " Fire a volley at that
belfry, and let the man who wants me have another
chance at me. I'll give the word. Make ready!"
I commanded.

There was a pause and a chorus of protests, and
then mechanically each man jerked out the empty
shell and drove the next cartridge in place.
"Aim!" I shouted. They hesitated and then
raised their pieces in a wavering line, and I looked
into the muzzles of a dozen rifles.

" Now then—damn you," I cried. " Fire!"

They fired, and my eyes and nostrils were filled
with burning smoke, but not a bullet had passed
near me.

" Again!" I shouted, stamping my foot. I was
so angry that I suppose I was really hardly ac-
countable for what I did.

" I told you you were cowards," I cried. "You
can only shoot men in the back. You don't like
me, don't you?" I cried, taunting them. " I'm
a braggart, am I? Yes. I'm a bully, am I? Well,

here's your chance. Get rid of me! Once again now. Make ready," I commanded. "Aim! Fire!"

Again the smoke swept up, and again I had escaped. I remember that I laughed at them and that the sound was crazy and hysterical, and I remember that as I laughed I shook out my arms to show them I was unhurt. And as I did that someone in the café cried, "Thank God!" And another shouted, "That's enough of this damn nonsense," and a big man with a bushy red beard sprang up and pulled off his hat.

"Now then," he cried. "All together, boys. Three cheers for the little one!" and they all jumped and shouted like mad people.

They cheered me again and again, although all the time the bullets from the belfry were striking about them, ringing on the iron tables and on the sidewalk, and tearing great gashes in the awnings overhead.

And then it seemed as though the sunlight on the yellow buildings and on the yellow earth of the plaza had been suddenly shut off, and I dropped into a well of blackness and sank deeper and deeper.

When I looked up the big man was sitting on the floor holding me as comfortably as though I were a baby, and my face was resting against his red beard, and my clothes and everything about me smelt terribly of brandy.

But the most curious thing about it was that though they told everyone in the Legion that I had stood up and made them shoot at me, they never let anyone find out that I had been so weak as to faint.

I do not know whether it was the brandy they gave me that later led me to charge those guns, but I appreciate now that my conduct was certainly silly and mad enough to be excused only in that way. According to the doctrine of chances I should have lost nine lives, and according to the rules governing an army in the field I should have been court-martialled. Instead of which, the men caught me up on their shoulders and carried me around the plaza, and Laguerre and Garcia looked on from the steps of the Cathedral and laughed and waved to us.

For five hours we had been lying in the blazing sun on the flat house-tops, or hidden in the shops around the plaza, and the government troops were still holding us off with one hand and spanking us with the other. Their guns were so good that, when Heinze attempted to take up a position against them with his old-style Gatlings, they swept him out of the street, as a fire-hose flushes a gutter. For five hours they had kept the plaza empty, and peppered the three sides of it so warmly that no one of us should have shown his head.

But at every shot from the Cathedral our men grew more unmanageable, and the longer the enemy held us back the more arrogant and defiant they became. Ostensibly to obtain a better shot, but in reality from pure deviltry, they would make individual sallies into the plaza, and, facing the embrasure, would empty their Winchesters at one of its openings as coolly as though they were firing at a painted bull's-eye. The man who first did this, the moment his rifle was empty, ran for cover and was tumultuously cheered by his hidden audience. But in order to surpass him, the next man, after he had emptied his gun, walked back very deliberately, and the third man remained to refill his magazine. And so a spirit of the most senseless rivalry sprang up, and one man after another darted out into the plaza to cap the recklessness of those who had gone before him.

It was not until five men were shot dead and lay sprawling and uncovered in the sun that the madness seemed to pass. But my charging the embrasure was always supposed to be a part of it, and to have been inspired entirely by vanity and a desire to do something more extravagantly reckless than any of the others. As a matter of fact I acted on what has always seemed to me excellent reasoning, and if I went alone, it was only because, having started, it seemed safer to go ahead than to run all the way back again. I never blamed the men for running back, and so I cannot see why they should blame me for having gone ahead.

The enemy had ceased firing shrapnel and were using solid shot. When their Gatlings also ceased, I guessed that it might be that the guns were jammed. If I were right and if one avoided the solid shot by approaching the barricade obliquely, there was no danger in charging the barricade.

I told my troop that I thought the guns were out of order, and that if we rushed the barricade we could take it. When I asked for volunteers, ten men came forward and at once, without asking permission, which I knew I could not get, we charged across the plaza.

Both sides saw us at the same instant, and the firing was so fierce that the men with me thought the Gatlings had reopened on us, and ran for cover.

That left me about fifty feet from the barricade, and as it seemed a toss-up whichever way I went I kept going forward. I caught the comb-

ing of the embrasure with my hands, stuck my
toes between the stones, and scrambled to the
top. The scene inside was horrible. The place
looked like a slaughter-yard. Only three men
were still on their legs; the rest were heaped
around the guns. I threatened the three men with
my revolver, but they shrieked for mercy and
I did not fire. The men in the belfries, however, were showing no mercy to me, so I dropped
inside the wall and crawled for shelter beneath
a caisson. But I recognized on the instant that
I could not remain there. It was the fear of
the Gatlings only which was holding back our
men, and I felt that before I was shot they must
know that the guns were jammed. So I again
scrambled up to the barricade, and waved my hat
to them to come on. At the same moment a
bullet passed through my shoulder, and another
burned my neck, and one of the men who had
begged for mercy beat me over the head with
his sword. I went down like a bag of flour, but
before my eyes closed I saw our fellows pour-
ing out of the houses and sweeping toward me.

About an hour later, when Von Ritter had
cleaned the hole in my shoulder and plastered my
skull, I sallied out again, and at sight of me the
men gave a shout, and picked me up, and, cheering, bore me around the plaza. From that day

we were the best of friends, and I think in time they grew to like me.

Two days later we pitched camp outside of Tegucigalpa, the promised city, the capital of the Republic.

Our points of attack were two: a stone bridge which joins the city proper with the suburbs, and a great hill of rock called El Pecachua. This hill either guards or betrays the capital. The houses reach almost to its base and from its crest one can drop a shell through the roof of any one of them. Consequently, when we arrived, we found its approaches strongly entrenched and the hill occupied in force by the government artillery. There is a saying in Honduras, which has been justified by countless revolutions, and which dates back to the days of Morazan the Liberator, that "He who takes Pecachua sleeps in the Palace."

Garcia's plan was for two days to bombard the city, and if, in that time, Alvarez had not surrendered, to attack El Pecachua by night. As usual, the work was so divided that the more dangerous and difficult part of it fell to the Foreign Legion, for in his plan Garcia so ordered it that Laguerre should storm Pecachua, while he advanced from the plain and attacked the city at the stone bridge.

But this plan was never carried out, and after our first day in front of the Capital, General Garcia never again gave an order to General Laguerre.

After midnight on the evening of that first day Aiken came to the hut where we had made our head-quarters and demanded to see the General on a matter of life and death. With him, looking very uncertain as to the propriety of the visit, were all the officers of the Legion.

The General was somewhat surprised and somewhat amused, but he invited us to enter. When the officers had lined up against the walls he said, "As a rule, I call my own councils of war, but no doubt Mr. Aiken has some very good reason for affording me the pleasure of your company. What is it, Mr. Aiken?"

Instead of answering him, Aiken said, with as much manner as that of General Garcia himself, "I want a guard put outside this house, and I want the men placed far enough from it to prevent their hearing what I say." The General nodded at me, and I ordered the sentries to move farther from the hut. I still remember the tableau I saw when I re-entered it, the row of officers leaning against the mud walls, the candles stuck in their own grease on the table, the maps spread over it, and the General and Aiken facing each other from its either end.   It looked like a drumhead court-martial.

When I had shut the door of the hut Aiken spoke.   His tone was one of calm unconcern.

"I have just come from the Palace," he said, "where I have been having a talk with President Alvarez."

No one made a sound, nor no one spoke, but like one man everyone in the room reached for his revolver.   It was a most enlightening revelation of our confidence in Aiken.   Laguerre did not move.   He was looking steadily at Aiken and his eyes were shining like two arc lamps.

"By whose authority?" he asked.

We, who knew every tone of his voice, almost felt sorry for Aiken.

"By whose authority," Laguerre repeated, "did you communicate with the enemy?"

"It was an idea of my own," Aiken answered simply.   "I was afraid if I told you you would interfere.   Oh! I'm no soldier," he said.   He was replying to the look in Laguerre's face. "And I can tell you that there are other ways of doing things than 'according to Hardie.'   Alvarez's officers came to me after the battle of Comyagua.   They expected to beat you there, and when you chased them out of the city and

started for the Capital they thought it was all up
with them, and decided to make terms."

" With you?" said Laguerre.

Aiken laughed without the least trace of resentment, and nodded.

" Well, you give a dog a bad name," he said,
" and it sticks to him. So, they came to me.
I'm no grand-stand fighter; I'm not a fighter at
all. I think fighting is silly. You've got all the
young men you want to stop bullets for you,
without me. They like it. They like to catch
'em in their teeth. I don't. But that's not saying that I'm no good. You know the old gag of
the lion and the little mousie, and how the mouse
came along and chewed the lion out of the net.
Well, that's me. I'm no lion going 'round seeking whom I may devour.' I'm just a sewer rat.
But I can tell you all," he cried, slapping the
table with his hand, " that, if it hadn't been for
little mousie, every one of you lions would have
been shot against a stone wall. And if I can't
prove it, you can take a shot at me. I've been
the traitor. I've been the go-between from the
first. I arranged the whole thing. The Alvarez
crowd told me to tell Garcia that even if he did
succeed in getting into the Palace the Isthmian
Line would drive him out of it in a week. But
that if he'd go away from the country, they'd pay

him fifty thousand pesos and a pension. He's got the Isthmian Line's promise in writing.

"This joint attack he's planned for Wednesday night is a fake. He doesn't mean to fight. Nobody means to fight except against you. Every soldier and every gun in the city is to be sent out to Pecachua to trap you into an ambush. Natives who pretend to have deserted from Alvarez are to lead you into it. That was an idea of mine. They thought it was very clever. Garcia is to make a pretence of attacking the bridge and a pretence of being driven back. Then messengers are to bring word that the Foreign Legion has been cut to pieces at Pecachua, and he is to disband his army, and tell every man to look out for himself.

"If you want proofs of this, I'll furnish them to any man here that you'll pick out. I told Alvarez that one of your officers was working against you with me, and that at the proper time I'd produce him. Now, you choose which officer that shall be. He can learn for himself that all I'm telling you is true. But that will take time!" Aiken cried, as Laguerre made a movement to interrupt him. "And if you want to get out of this fix alive, you'd better believe me, and start for the coast at once—now—to-night!"

Laguerre laughed and sprang to his feet. His

eyes were shining and the color had rushed to his cheeks. He looked like a young man masquerading in a white wig. He waved his hand at Aiken with a gesture that was part benediction and part salute.

"I do believe you," he cried, "and thank you, sir." He glanced sharply at the officers around him as though he were weighing the value of each.

"Gentlemen," he cried, "often in my life I have been prejudiced, and often I have been deceived, and I think that it is time now that I acted for myself. From the first, the burden of this expedition has been carried by the Foreign Legion. I know that; you, who fought the battles, certainly know it. We invaded Honduras with a purpose. We came to obtain for the peons the debt that is due them and to give them liberty and free government. And whether our allies run away or betray us, that purpose is still the same."

He paused as though for the first time it had occurred to him that the motives of the others might not be as his own.

"Am I right?" he asked, eagerly. "Are you willing to carry out that purpose?" he demanded. "Are you ready to follow me now, to-night— not to the coast"—he shouted—"but to the Capital—to the top of Pecachua?"

Old man Webster jumped in front of us, and shot his arm into the air as though it held a standard.

" We'll follow you to hell and back again," he cried.

I would not have believed that so few men could have made so much noise. We yelled and cheered so wildly that we woke the camp. We could hear the men running down the road, and the sentries calling upon them to halt. The whole Legion was awake and wondering. Webster beat us into silence by pounding the table with his fist.

" I have lived in this country for forty years," he cried, with his eyes fixed upon Laguerre, " and you are the first white man I have known who has not come into it, either flying from the law, or to rob and despoil it. I know this country. I know all of Central America, and it is a wonderful country. There is not a fruit nor a grain nor a plant that you cannot dig out of it with your bare fingers. It has great forests, great pasture-lands, and buried treasures of silver and iron and gold. But it is cursed with the laziest of God's creatures, and the men who rule them are the most corrupt and the most vicious. They are the dogs in the manger among rulers. They will do nothing to help their own country ; they will not permit others to help it. They are a menace and an insult to civilization, and it is time that they stepped down and out, and made way for their betters, or that they were kicked out. One strong man, if he is an honest man, can conquer and hold Central America. William Walker was such a man. I was with him when he ruled the best part of this country for two years. He governed all Nicaragua with two hundred white men, and never before or since have the pueblo known such peace and justice and prosperity as Walker gave them."

Webster threw himself across the table and pointed his hand at Laguerre.

"And you, General Laguerre!" he cried, "and you? Do you see your duty? You say it calls you to-night to El Pecachua. Then if it does, it calls you farther—to the Capital! There can be no stopping half-way now, no turning back. If we follow you to-night to Pecachua, we follow you to the Palace."

Webster's voice rose until it seemed to shake the palm-leaf roof. He was like a man possessed. He sprang up on the table, and from the height above us hurled his words at Laguerre.

"We are not fighting for any half-breed now," he cried; "we are fighting for you. We know you. We believe in you. We mean to make you President, and we will not stop there. Our motto shall be Walker's motto, 'Five or none,' and when we have taken this Republic we shall take the other four, and you will be President of the United States of Central America."

We had been standing open-eyed, open-mouthed, every nerve trembling, and at these words we shrieked and cheered, but Webster waved at us with an angry gesture and leaned toward Laguerre.

"You will open this land," he cried, "with roads and railways. You will feed the world with its coffee. You will cut the Nicaragua Canal. And you will found an empire—not the empire of slaves that Walker planned, but an empire of freed men, freed by you from their tyrants and from themselves. They tell me, General," he cried, "that you have fought under thirteen flags. To-night, sir, you shall fight under your own!"

We all cheered and cheered again, the oldest as well as myself, and I cheered louder than any, until I looked at Laguerre. Then I felt how terribly real it was to him. Until I looked at him it had seemed quite sane and feasible. But when I saw how deeply he was moved, and that his eyes were brimming with pride and resolve, I

felt that it was a mad dream, and that we were
wicked not to wake him. For I, who loved him
like a son, understood what it meant to him. In
his talk along the trail and by the camp-fire he
had always dreamed of an impossible republic, an
Utopia ruled by love and justice, and I now saw
he believed that the dreams had at last come
true. I knew that the offer these men had made
to follow him, filled him with a great happiness
and gratitude. And that he, who all his life had
striven so earnestly and so loyally for others,
would give his very soul for men who fought
for him. I was not glad that they had offered
to make him their leader. I could only look
ahead with miserable forebodings and feel bitterly sorry that one so fine and good was again
to be disillusioned and disappointed and cast
down.

But there was no time that night to look
ahead. The men were outside the hut, a black,
growling mob crying for revenge upon Garcia.
Had we not at once surrounded them they would
have broken for his camp and murdered him in
his hammock, and with him his ignorant, deceived
followers.

But when Webster spoke to them as he had
spoken to us, and told them what we planned to
do, and Laguerre stepped out into the moon-

light, they forgot their anger in their pride for him, and at his first word they fell into the ranks as obediently as so many fond and devoted children.

In Honduras a night attack is a discredited manœuvre. It is considered an affront to the Blessed Virgin, who first invented sleep. And those officers who that night guarded Pecachua, being acquainted with Garcia's plot, were not expecting us until two nights later, when we were to walk into their parlor, and be torn to pieces. Consequently, when Miller, who knew Pecachua well, having served without political prejudice in six revolutions, led us up a by-path to its top, we found the government troops sleeping sweetly. Before their only sentry had discovered that someone was kneeling on his chest, our men were in possession of their batteries.

That morning when the sun rose gloriously, as from a bath, all pink and shining and dripping with radiance, and the church bells began to clang for early mass, and the bugles at the barracks sounded the jaunty call of the reveille, two puffs of white smoke rose from the crest of El Pecachua and drifted lazily away. At the same instant a shell sang over the roofs of Tegucigalpa, howling jeeringly, and smashed into the pots and pans of the President's kitchen; another, falling two miles farther to the right, burst through the white tent of General Garcia, and the people in the streets, as they crossed themselves in fear, knew that El Pecachua had again been taken, and that that night a new President would sleep in the Palace.

All through the hot hours of the morning the captured guns roared and echoed, until at last we saw Garcia's force crawling away in a crowd of dust toward the hills, and an hour later Alvarez, with the household troops, abandoning the Capital and hastening after him.

We were too few to follow, but we whipped them forward with our shells.

A half-hour later a timid group of merchants and foreign consuls, led by the Bishop and bearing a great white flag, rode out to the foot of the rock and surrendered the city.

I am sure no government was ever established more quickly than ours. We held our first cabinet meeting twenty minutes after we entered the capital, and ten minutes later Webster, from the balcony of the Palace, proclaimed Laguerre President and Military Dictator of Honduras. Laguerre in turn nominated Webster, on account of his knowledge of the country, Minister of the Interior, and made me Vice-President and Minister of War. No one knew what were the duties of a Vice-President, so I asked if I might not also be Provost-Marshal of the city, and I was accordingly appointed to that position and sent out into the street to keep order.

Aiken, as a reward for his late services, was made head of the detective department and Chief of Police. His first official act was to promote two bare-footed policemen who on his last visit to the Capital had put him under arrest.

The General, or the President, as we now called him, at once issued a ringing proclamation in which he promised every liberty that the people of a free republic should enjoy, and announced that in three months he would call a general election, when the people could either re-elect him, or a candidate of their own choice. He announced also that he would force the Isthmian Line to pay the people the half million of dollars it owed them, and he suggested that this money be placed to the credit of the people, and that they should pay no taxes until the sum was consumed in public improvements. Up to that time every new President had imposed new taxes; none had ever suggested remitting them altogether, and this offer made a tremendous sensation in our favor.

There were other departures from the usual

procedure of victorious presidents which helped much to make us popular. One was the fact that Laguerre did not shoot anybody against the barrack wall, nor levy forced "loans" upon the foreign merchants. Indeed, the only persons who suffered on the day he came into power were two of our own men, whom I caught looting. I put them to sweeping the streets, each with a ball and chain to his ankle, as an example of the sort of order we meant to keep among ourselves.

Before mid-day Aiken sent a list, which his spies had compiled, of sympathizers with Alvarez. He guaranteed to have them all in jail before night. But Laguerre sent for them and promised them, if they remained neutral, they should not be molested. Personally, I have always been of the opinion that most of the persons on Aiken's list of suspects were most worthy merchants, to whom he owed money.

Laguerre gave a long audience to the cashier of the Manchester and Central American Bank, Limited, which finances Honduras, and assured him that the new administration would not force the bank to accept the paper money issued by Alvarez, but would accept the paper money issued by the bank, which was based on gold. As a result, the cashier came down the stair-case of the Palace three steps at a time, and later our censor read his cable to the Home Bank in England, in which he said that Honduras at last had an honest man for President. What was more to the purpose, he reopened his bank at three o'clock, and quoted Honduranian money on his blackboard at a rise of three per cent. over that of the day before. This was a great compliment to our government, and it must have impressed the other business men, for by six o'clock that night a delegation of American, German, and English shopkeepers called on the President and offered him a vote of confidence. They volunteered also to form a home-guard for the defence of the city, and to help keep him in office.

So, by dinner-time, we had won over the foreign element entirely, and the consuls had cabled their several ministers, advising them to advise their governments to recognize ours.

It was a great triumph ror fair promises backed by fair dealing.

Although I was a cabinet minister and had a right to have my say I did not concern myself much with these graver problems of the Palace.

Instead, my first act was to cable to Beatrice that we were safe in the Capital and that I was second in command. I did not tell her I was Vice-President of a country of 300,000 people, because at Dobbs Ferry such a fact would seem hardly probable. After that I spent the day very happily galloping around the town with the Provost Guard at my heels, making friends with the inhabitants, and arranging for their defence. I posted a gun at the entrance to each of the three principal streets, and ordered mounted scouts to patrol the plains outside the Capital. I also remembered Heinze and the artillerymen who were protecting us on the heights of Pecachua, and sent them a moderate amount of rum, and an immoderate amount of canned goods and cigars. I also found time to design a wonderful uniform for the officers of our Legion—a dark-green blouse with silver facings and scarlet riding breeches—and on the plea of military necessity I ordered six tailors to sit up all night to finish them.

Uniforms for the men I requisitioned from the stores of the Government, and ordered the red facings changed to yellow.

The next day when we paraded in full dress the President noticed this, and remarked, " No one but Macklin could have converted a battery of artillery, without the loss of a single gun or the addition of a single horse, into a battalion of cavalry."

We had escorted the President back to the Palace, and I was returning to the barracks at the

head of the Legion, with the local band playing
grandly before me, and the people bowing from
the sidewalks, when a girl on a gray pony turned
into the plaza and rode toward us.

She was followed by a group of white men, but
I saw only the girl. When I recognized even at
a distance that she was a girl from the States my
satisfaction was unbounded. It had needed only
the presence of such an audience to give the final
touch of pleasure to my triumphant progress.
My new uniform had been finished only just in
time.

When I first saw the girl I was startled merely
because any white woman in Honduras is an
unusual spectacle, but as she rode nearer I knew
that, had I seen this girl at home among a thousand women, I would have looked only at her.

She wore a white riding-habit, and a high-
peaked Mexican sombrero, and when her pony
shied at the sound of the music she raised her
head, and the sun struck on the burnished braid
around the brim, and framed her face with a rim
of silver. I had never seen such a face. It was
so beautiful that I drew a great breath of wonder,
and my throat tightened with the deep delight
that rose in me.

I stared at her as she rode forward, because I
could not help myself. If an earthquake had

opened a crevasse at my feet I would not have lowered my eyes. I had time to guess who she was, for I knew there could be no other woman so beautiful in Honduras, except the daughter of Joseph Fiske. Had not Aiken said of her, " When she passes, the native women kneel by the trail and cross themselves ? "

I rode toward her fearfully, conscious only of a sudden deep flood of gratitude for anything so nobly beautiful. I was as humbly thankful as the crusader who is rewarded by his first sight of the Holy City, and I was glad, too, that I came into her presence worthily, riding in advance of a regiment. I was proud of our triumphant music, of our captured flags and guns, and the men behind me, who had taken them.

I still watched her as our column drew nearer, and she pulled her pony to one side to let it pass. I felt as though I were marching in review before an empress, and I all but lifted my sword-blade in salute.

But as we passed I saw that the look on her face was that of a superior and critical adversary. It was a glance of amused disdain, softened only by a smile of contempt. As it fell upon me I blushed to the rim of my sombrero. I felt as meanly as though I had been caught in a lie. With her eyes, I saw the bare feet of our negro band, our ill-fitting uniforms with their flannel facings, the swagger of our officers, glancing pompously from their half-starved, unkempt ponies upon the native Indians, who fawned at us from the sidewalks.

I saw that to her we were so many red-shirted firemen, dragging a wooden hose-cart; a company of burnt-cork minstrels, kicking up the dust of a village street; that we were ridiculous, lawless, absurd, and it was like a blow over my heart that one so noble-looking should be so blind and so unjust. I was swept with bitter indignation. I wanted to turn in my saddle and cry to her that beneath the flannel facings at which she laughed these men wore deep, uncared-for, festering wounds; that to march thus through the streets of this tiny Capital they had waded waist-high through rivers, had starved in fever camps, and at any hour when I had called on them had run forward to throw cold hands with death.

The group of gentlemen who were riding with the girl had halted their ponies by the sidewalk, and as I drew near I noted that one of them wore the uniform of an ensign in our navy. This puzzled me for an instant, until I remembered I had heard that the cruiser Raleigh was lying at Amapala. I was just passing the group when one of them, with the evident intent that I should hear him, raised his voice.

"Well, here's the army," he said, "but where's Falstaff? I don't see Laguerre."

My face was still burning with the blush the girl had brought to it, and the moment was not the one that any man should have chosen to ridicule my general. Because the girl had laughed at us I felt indignant with her, but for the same offence I was grateful to the man, for the reason that he was a man, and could be punished. I whirled my pony around and rode it close against his.

"You must apologize for that," I said, speaking in a low voice, "or I'll thrash you with this riding-whip."

He was a young man, exceedingly well-looking, slim and tall, and with a fine air of good breeding. He looked straight into my eyes without moving. His hands remained closed upon the pommel of his saddle.

"If you raise that whip," he said, "I'll take your tin sword away from you, and spank you with it."

Never in my life had anyone hurt me so terribly. And the insult had come before my men and his friends and the people in the street. It turned me perfectly cold, and all the blood seemed to run to my eyes, so that I saw everything in a red haze. When I answered him my voice sounded hoarse and shaky.

" Get down," I said. " Get down, or I'll pull you down. I'm going to thrash you until you can't stand or see."

He struck at me with his riding-crop, but I caught him by the collar and with an old trick of the West Point riding-hall threw him off into the street, and landed on my feet above him. At the same moment Miller and Von Ritter drove their ponies in between us, and three of the man's friends pushed in from the other side. But in spite of them we reached each other, and I struck up under his guard and beat him savagely on the face and head, until I found his chin, and he went down. There was an awful row. The whole street was in an uproar, women screamed, the ponies were rearing and kicking, the natives jabbering, and my own men swearing and struggling in a ring around us.

" My God, Macklin ! " I heard Von Ritter cry, " stop it ! Behave yourself ! "

He rode at our men with his sword and drove them back into ranks. I heard him shout, " Fall in there. Forward. March ! "

" This is your idea of keeping order, is it ? " Miller shouted at me.

" He insulted Laguerre," I shouted back, and scrambled into the saddle. But I was far from satisfied. I, Vice-President, Minister of War,

Provost-Marshal of the city, had been fighting with my fists in the open street before half the population. I knew what Laguerre would say, and I wondered hotly if the girl had seen me, and I swore at myself for having justified her contempt for us. Then I swore at myself again for giving a moment's consideration to what she thought. I was recalled to the present by the apparition of my adversary riding his pony toward me, partly supported and partly restrained by two of his friends. He was trembling with anger and pain and mortification.

"You shall fight me for this," he cried.

I was about to retort that he looked as though I had been fighting him, but it is not easy to laugh at a man when he is covered with dust and blood, and this one was so sorry a spectacle that I felt ashamed for him, and said nothing.

"I am not a street fighter," he raged. "I wasn't taught to fight in a lot. But I'll fight you like a gentleman, just as though you were a gentleman. You needn't think you've heard the last of me. My friends will act for me, and, unless you're a coward, you will name your seconds."

Before I could answer, Von Ritter had removed his hat and was bowing violently from his saddle.

"I am Baron Herbert Von Ritter," he said, "late Aide-de-Camp to his Majesty, the King of

Captain Macklin

Bavaria. If you are not satisfied, Captain Miller
and myself will do ourselves the honor of calling
on your friends."

His manner was so grand that it quite calmed
me to hear him.

One of the men who was supporting my adversary, a big, sun-burned man, in a pith helmet,
shook his head violently.

"Here, none of that, Miller," he said; "drop
it. Can't you see the boy isn't himself? This
isn't the time to take advantage of him."

"We are only trying to oblige the gentleman,"
said Miller. "The duel is the only means of
defence we've left you people. But I tell you, if
any of you insult our government again, we won't
even give you that satisfaction—we'll ride you
out of town."

The man in the pith helmet listened to Miller
without any trace of emotion. When Miller had
finished he laughed.

"We've every means of defence that an American citizen needs when he runs up against a
crowd like yours," he said. He picked up his
reins and turned his horse's head down the street.
"You will find us at the Hotel Continental," he
added. "And as for running us out of town,"
he shouted over his shoulder, "there's an American man-of-war at Amapala that is going to

213

chase you people out of it as soon as we give the word."

When I saw that Miller and Von Ritter were arranging a duel, I felt no further interest in what the man said, until he threatened us with the warship. At that I turned toward the naval ensign to see how he received it.

He was a young man, some years older than myself, with a smooth face and fair, yellow hair and blue eyes. I found that the blue eyes were fixed upon me steadily and kindly. When he saw that I had caught him watching me he raised his hand smartly to the visor.

I do not know why, but it made the tears come to my eyes. It was so different from the salute of our own men; it was like being back again under the flag at the Point. It was the recognition of the "regular" that touched me, of a bona-fide, commissioned officer.

But I returned his salute just as stiffly as though I were a commissioned officer myself. And then a strange thing happened. The sailor-boy jerked his head toward the retreating form of my late adversary, and slowly stuck his tongue into his cheek, and winked. Before I could recover myself, he had caught up my hand and given it a sharp shake, and galloped after his friends.

Captain Macklin

Miller and I fell in at the rear of the column.

" Who were those men ? " I asked.

" The Isthmian Line people, of course," he answered, shortly. " The man in the helmet is Graham, the manager of the Copan Silver Mines. They've just unloaded them on Fiske. That's why they're so thick with him."

" And who was the chap who insulted Laguerre ? " I asked. " The one whose face I slapped ? "

" Face you slapped ? Ha ! " Miller snorted. " I hope you'll never slap my face. Why, don't you know who he is ? " he exclaimed, with a grin. " I thought, of course, you did. I thought that's why you hit him. He's young Fiske, the old man's son. That was his sister riding ahead of them. Didn't you see that girl ? "

V

THE day we attacked the capital Joseph Fiske and his party were absent from it, visiting Graham, the manager of the Copan Mines, at his country place, and when word was received there that we had taken the city, Graham urged Mr. Fiske not to return to it, but to ride at once to the coast and go on board the yacht. They told him that the capital was in the hands of a mob.

But what really made Graham, and the rest of the Copan people, and the Isthmian crowd, who now were all working together against us, so anxious to get Fiske out of Honduras, was that part of Laguerre's proclamation in which he said he would force the Isthmian Line to pay its just debts. They were most anxious that Fiske should not learn from us the true version of that claim for back pay. They had told him we were a lot of professional filibusters, that the demand we made for the half-million of dollars was a gigantic attempt at blackmail. They pointed out to him that the judges of the highest courts of Honduras had decided against the validity of our claim, but they did not tell him that Alvarez had ordered the judges to decide in favor of the company, nor how much money they had paid Alvarez and the judges for that decision. Instead they urged that Garcia, a native of the country, had submitted to the decree of the courts and had joined Alvarez, and that now the only people fighting against the Isthmian Line were foreign adventurers. They asked, Was it likely such men would risk their lives to benefit the natives? Was it not evident that they were fighting only for their own pockets? And they warned Fiske that while Laguerre was still urging his claim against this company, it would be unwise for the president of that company to show himself in Tegucigalpa.

But Fiske laughed at the idea of danger to himself. He said a revolution, like cock-fighting, was a national pastime, and no more serious, and that should anyone attempt to molest the property of the company, he would demand the protection of his own country as represented by the Raleigh.

He accordingly rode back to the capital, and with his son and daughter and the company's representatives and the Copan people, returned to the same rooms in the Hotel Continental he had occupied three days before, when Alvarez was president. This made it embarrassing for us, as the Continental was the only hotel in the city, and as it was there we had organized our officers' mess. In consequence, while there was no open war, the dining-room of the hotel was twice daily the meeting-place of the two opposing factions, and Von Ritter told me that until matters had been arranged with the seconds of young Fiske I could not appear there, as it would be "contrary to the code."

But our officers were not going to allow the Copan and Isthmian people to drive them out of their head-quarters, so at the table d'hôte luncheon that day our fellows sat at one end of the room, and Fiske and Miss Fiske, Graham and his followers at the other. They entirely ignored each other. After the row I had raised in the street, each side was anxious to avoid further friction.

As I sat in the barracks over my solitary luncheon my thoughts were entirely on the duel.

It had been forced on me, so I accepted it; but it struck me as a most silly proceeding. Young Fiske had insulted my General and my comrades. He had done so publicly and with intent. I had thrashed him as I said I would, and as far as I could see the incident was closed. But Miller and Von Ritter, who knew Honduras from Fonseca Bay to Truxillo, assured me that, unless I met the man, who had insulted me before the people, our prestige would be entirely destroyed. To the Honduranian mind, the fact that I had thrashed him for so doing, would not serve as a substitute for a duel, it only made a duel absolutely necessary. As I had determined, if we did meet, that I would not shoot at him, I knew I would receive no credit from such an encounter, and, so far as I could see, I was being made ridiculous, and stood a very fair chance of being killed.

I sincerely hoped that young Fiske would apologize. I assured myself that my reluctance to meet him was due to the fact that I scorned to fight a civilian. I always classed civilians, with women and children, as non-combatants. But in my heart I knew that it was not this prejudice which made me hesitate. The sister was the real reason. That he was her brother was the only fact of importance. Had his name been Robinson or Brown, I would have gone out and shot at the calves of his legs most cheerfully, and taken considerable satisfaction in the notoriety that would have followed my having done so.

But I could never let his sister know that I had only fired in the air, and I knew that if I fought her brother she would always look upon me as one who had attempted to murder him. I could never speak to her, or even look at her again. And at that moment I felt that if I did not meet her, I could go without meeting any other women for many years to come. She was the most wonderful creature I had ever seen. She was not beautiful, as Beatrice was beautiful, in a womanly, gracious way, but she had the beauty of something unattainable. Instead of inspiring you, she filled you with disquiet. She seemed to me a regal, goddess-like woman, one that a man might worship with that tribute of fear and adoration that savages pay to the fire and the sun.

I had ceased to blush because she had laughed at us. I had begun to think that it was quite right that she should do so. To her we were lawless adventurers, exiles, expatriates, fugitives. She did not know that most of us were unselfish, and that our cause was just. She thought, if she thought of us at all, that we were trying to levy blackmail on her father. I did not blame her for despising us. I only wished I could tell her how she had been deceived, and assure her that among us there was one, at least, who thought of her gratefully and devotedly, and who would suffer much before he would hurt her or hers. I knew that this was so, and I hoped her brother would not be such an ass as to insist upon a duel, and make me pretend to fight him, that her father would be honest enough to pay his debts, and that some day she and I might be friends.

But these hopes were killed by the entrance of Miller and Von Ritter. They looked very grave.

" He won't apologize," Miller said. " We arranged that you are to meet behind the grave-vard at sunrise to-morrow morning." I was bit-terly disappointed, but of course I could not let them see that.

" Does Laguerre know?" I asked.

" No," Miller said, "neither does old man Fiske. We had the deuce of a time. Graham and Lowell—that young Middy from the Raleigh —are his seconds, and we found we were all agreed that he had better apologize. Lowell, especially, was very keen that you two should shake hands, but when they went out to talk it over with Fiske, he came back with them in a terrible rage, and swore he'd not apologize, and that he'd either shoot you or see you hung. Lowell told him it was all rot that two Americans should be fighting duels, but Fiske said that when he was in Rome, he did as Romans did; that he had been brought up in Paris to believe in duels, and that a duel he would have. Then the sister came in, and there was a hell of a row!"

" The sister ! " I exclaimed.

Miller nodded, and Von Ritter and he shook their heads sadly at each other, as though the recollection of the interview weighed heavily.

" Yes, his sister," said Miller. " You know how these Honduranian places are built, if a parrot scratches his feathers in the patio you can hear it in every room in the house. Well, she was reading on the balcony, and when her brother began to rage around and swear he'd have your blood, she heard him, and opened the shutters and came in. She didn't stay long, and she didn't say much, but she talked to us as though we were so many bad children. I never felt so mean in my life."

" She should not have been there," said Von Ritter, stolidly. " It was most irregular."

" Fiske tried the high and mighty, brotherly act with her," Miller continued, " but she shook him up like a charge of rack-a-rock. She told him that a duel was unmanly and un-American, and that he would be a murderer. She said his honor didn't require him to risk his life for every cad who went about armed, insulting unarmed people——"

" What did she say?" I cried. "Say that again."

Von Ritter tossed up his arms and groaned, but Miller shook his fist at me.

"Now, don't you go and get wrathy," he roared. "We'll not stand it. We've been abused by everybody else on your account to-day, and we won't take it from you. It doesn't matter what the girl said. They probably told her you began the fight, and——"

"She said I was a cad," I repeated, "and that I struck an unarmed man. Didn't her brother tell her that he first insulted me, and struck me with his whip, and that I only used my fists. Didn't any of you tell her?"

"No!" roared Miller; "what the devil has that got to do with it? She was trying to prevent the duel. We were trying to prevent the duel. That's all that's important. And if she hadn't made the mistake of thinking you might back out of it, we could have prevented it. Now we can't."

I began to wonder if the opinion the Fiske family had formed of me, on so slight an acquaintance, was not more severe than I deserved, but I did not let the men see how sorely the news had hurt me. I only asked: "What other mistake did the young lady make?"

"She meant it all right," said Miller, "but it was a woman's idea of a bluff, and it didn't go. She told us that before we urged her brother on to fight, we should have found out that he has spent the last five years in Paris, and that he's the gilt-edged pistol-shot of the *salle d'armes* in the Rue Scribe, that he can hit a scarf-pin at twenty paces. Of course that ended it. The Baron spoke up in his best style and said that in the face of this information it would be now quite impossible for our man to accept an apology without being considered a coward, and that a meeting must take place. Then the girl ran to her brother and said, 'What have I done?' and he put his arm around her and walked her out of the room. Then we arranged the details in peace and came on here."

"Good," I said, "you did exactly right. I'll meet you at dinner at the hotel."

But at this Von Ritter protested that I must not dine there, that it was against the code.

"The code be hanged," I said. "If I don't turn up at dinner they'll say I'm afraid to show myself out of doors. Besides, if I must be shot through the scarf-pin before breakfast to-morrow morning, I mean to have a good dinner to-night."

They left me, and I rode to the palace to make my daily report to the president. I was relieved to find that both he and Webster were so deep in affairs of state that they had heard nothing of my row in the Plaza, nor of the duel to follow. They were happy as two children building forts of sand on the sea-shore. They had rescinded taxes, altered the tariffs, reorganized the law-courts, taken over the custom-houses by telegraph, and every five minutes were receiving addresses from delegations of prominent Honduranians. Nicaragua and Salvador had both recognized their government, and concession hunters were already cooling their heels in the ante-room. In every town and seaport the adherents of Garcia had swung over to Laguerre and our government, and our flag was now flying in every part of Honduras. It was the flag of Walker, with the five-pointed blood-red star. We did not explain the significance of the five points.

I reported that my scouts had located Alvarez and Garcia in the hills some five miles distant from the capital, that they were preparing a permanent camp there, and that they gave no evidence of any immediate intention of attacking the city. General Laguerre was already informed of the arrival of Mr. Fiske, and had arranged to give him an audience the following morning. He hoped in this interview to make clear to him how just was the people's claim for the half million due them, and to obtain his guaranty that the money should be paid.

As I was leaving the palace I met Aiken. He

was in his most cynical mood. He said that the air was filled with plots and counter-plots, and that treachery stalked abroad. He had been unsuccessful in trying to persuade the president to relieve Heinze of his command on Pecachua. He wanted Von Ritter or myself put in his place.

"It is the key to the position," Aiken said, "and if Heinze should sell us out, we would have to run for our lives. These people are all smiles and 'vivas' to-day because we are on top. But if we lost Pecachua, every man of them would turn against us."

I laughed and said: "We can trust Heinze. If I had your opinion of my fellow-man, I'd blow my brains out."

"If I hadn't had such a low opinion of my fellow-man," Aiken retorted, "he'd have blown your brains out. Don't forget that."

"No one listens to me," he said. "I consider that I am very hardly used. For a consideration a friend of Alvarez told me where Alvarez had buried most of the government money. I went to the cellar and dug it up and turned it over to Laguerre. And what do you think he's doing with it!" Aiken exclaimed with indignation. "He's going to give the government troops their back pay, and the post-office clerks, and the peons who worked on the public roads."

I said I considered that that was a most excellent use to make of the money; that from what I had seen of the native troops, it would turn our prisoners of war into our most loyal adherents.

"Of course it will!" Aiken agreed. "Why, if the government troops out there in the hills with Alvarez knew we were paying sixty pesos for soldiers, they'd run to join us so quick that they'd die on the way of sunstroke. But that's not it. Where do we come in? What do we get out of this? Have we been fighting for three months just to pay the troops who have been fighting against us? Charity begins at home, I think."

"You get your own salary, don't you?" I asked.

"Oh, I'm not starving," Aiken said, with a grin. "There's a lot of loot in being chief-of-police. This is going to be a wide-open town if I can run it."

"Well, you can't," I laughed. "Not as long as I'm its provost marshal."

"Yes, and how long will that be?" Aiken retorted. "You take my advice and make money now, while you've got the club to get it with you. Why, if I had your job I could scare ten thousand sols out of these merchants before sunrise. Instead of which you walk around nights to see their front doors are locked. Let them do the walking.

We've won, and let's enjoy the spoil. Eat, live and be merry, my boy, for to-morrow you die."

"I hope not," I exclaimed, and I ran down the steps of the palace and turned toward the barracks.

"To-morrow you die," I repeated, but I could not arouse a single emotion. Portents and premonitions may frighten some people, but the only superstition I hold to is to believe in the luck of Royal Macklin.

"What if Fiske can hit a scarf-pin at twenty paces!" I said to myself, "he can't hit me." I was just as sure of it as I was of the fact that when I met him I was going to fire in the air. I cannot tell why. I was just sure of it.

The dining-room at the Continental held three long tables. That night our officers sat at one, Mr. Fiske and his party were at the one farthest away, and a dining-club of consular agents, merchants, and the Telegraph Company's people occupied the one in between. I could see her whenever the German consul bent over his food. She was very pale and tired-looking, but in the white evening frock she wore, all soft and shining with lace, she was as beautiful as the moonlit night outside. She never once looked in our direction. But I could not keep my eyes away from her. The merchants, no doubt, enjoyed their dinner. They laughed and argued boisterously, but at the two other tables there was very little said.

The waiters, pattering over the stone floor in their bare feet, made more noise than our entire mess.

When the brandy came, Russell nodded at the others, and they filled their glasses and drank to me in silence. At the other table I saw the same pantomime, only on account of old man Fiske they had to act even more covertly. It struck me as being vastly absurd and wicked. What right had young Fiske to put his life in jeopardy to me? It was not in my keeping. I had no claim upon it. It was not in his own keeping. At least not to throw away.

When they had gone and our officers had shaken hands with me and ridden off to their different posts, I went out upon the balcony by myself and sat down in the shadow of the vines. The stream which cuts Tegucigalpa in two ran directly below the hotel, splashing against the rocks and sweeping under the stone bridge with a ceaseless murmur. Beyond it stretched the red-tiled roofs, glowing pink in the moonlight, and beyond them the camp-fires of Alvarez twinkling like glow-worms against the dark background of the hills. The town had gone to sleep, and the hotel was as silent as a church. There was no

sound except the whistle of a policeman calling
the hour, the bark of the street-dogs in answer,
and the voice of one of our sentries, arguing with
some jovial gentleman who was abroad without a
pass. After the fever and anxieties of the last
few days the peace of the moment was sweet and
grateful to me, and I sank deeper into the long
wicker chair and sighed with content. The previous night I had spent on provost duty in the
saddle, and it must have been that I dropped
asleep, for when I next raised my head Miss
Fiske was standing not twenty feet from me. She
was leaning against one of the pillars, a cold and
stately statue in the moonlight.

She did not know anyone was near her, and
when I moved and my spurs clanked on the
stones, she started, and turned her eyes slowly
toward the shadow in which I sat.

During dinner they must have told her which
one of us was to fight the duel, for when she
recognized me she moved sharply away. I did
not wish her to think I would intrude on her
against her will, so I rose and walked toward the
door, but before I had reached it she again turned
and approached me.

"You are Captain Macklin?" she said.

I was so excited at the thought that she was
about to speak to me, and so happy to hear her

voice, that for an instant I could only whip off my hat and gaze at her stupidly.

"Captain Macklin," she repeated. "This afternoon I tried to stop the duel you are to fight with my brother, and I am told that I made a very serious blunder. I should like to try and correct it. When I spoke of my brother's skill, I mean his skill with the pistol, I knew you were ignorant of it and I thought if you did know of it you would see the utter folly, the wickedness of this duel. But instead I am told that I only made it difficult for you not to meet him. I cannot in the least see that that follows. I wish to make it clear to you that it does not."

She paused, and I, as though I had been speaking, drew a long breath. Had she been reading from a book her tone could not have been more impersonal. I might have been one of a class of school-boys to whom she was expounding a problem. At the Point I have heard officers' wives use the same tone to the enlisted men. Its effect on them was to drive them into a surly silence.

But Miss Fiske did not seem conscious of her tone.

"After I had spoken," she went on evenly, "they told me of your reputation in this country, that you are known to be quite fearless. They told me of your ordering your own men to shoot you, and of how you took a cannon with your hands. Well, I cannot see—since your reputation for bravery is so well established—that you need to prove it further, certainly not by engaging in a silly duel. You cannot add to it by fighting my brother, and if you should injure him, you would bring cruel distress to—to others."

" I assure you——" I began.

" Pardon me," she said, raising her hand, but still speaking in the same even tone. " Let me explain myself fully. Your own friends said in my hearing," she went on, " that they did not desire a fight. It is then my remark only which apparently makes it inevitable."

She drew herself up and her tone grew even more distant and disdainful.

" Now, it is not possible," she exclaimed, " that you and your friends are going to take advantage of my mistake, and make it the excuse for this meeting. Suppose any harm should come to my brother." For the first time her voice carried a touch of feeling. " It would be my fault. I would always have myself to blame. And I want to ask you not to fight him. I want to ask you to withdraw from this altogether."

I was completely confused. Never before had a young lady of a class which I had so seldom met, spoken to me even in the words of every-day civility, and now this one, who was the most wonderful and beautiful woman I had ever seen, was asking me to grant an impossible favor, was speaking of my reputation for bravery as though it were a fact which everyone accepted, and was begging me not to make her suffer. What added to my perplexity was that she asked me to act only as I desired to act, but she asked it in such a manner that every nerve in me rebelled.

I could not understand how she could ask so great a favor of one she held in such evident contempt. It seemed to me that she should not have addressed me at all, or if she did ask me to stultify my honor and spare the life of her precious brother she should not have done so in the same tone with which she would have asked a tradesman for his bill. The fact that I knew, since I meant to fire in the air, that the duel was a farce, made it still more difficult for me to speak.

But I managed to say that what she asked was impossible.

" I do not know," I stammered, " that I ought to talk about it to you at all. But you don't understand that your brother did not only insult me. He insulted my regiment, and my general. It was that I resented, and that is why I am fighting."

"Then you refuse?" she said.

"I have no choice," I replied; "he has left me no choice."

She drew back, but still stood looking at me coldly. The dislike in her eyes wounded me inexpressively.

Before she spoke I had longed only for the chance to assure her of my regard, and had she appealed to me generously, in a manner suited to one so noble-looking, I was in a state of mind to swim rivers and climb mountains to serve her. I still would have fought the duel, but sooner than harm her brother I would have put my hand in the fire. Now, since she had spoken, I was filled only with pity and disappointment. It seemed so wrong that one so finely bred and wonderfully fair should feel so little consideration. No matter how greatly she had been prejudiced against me she had no cause to ignore my rights in the matter. To speak to me as though I had no honor of my own, no worthy motive, to treat me like a common brawler who, because his vanity was wounded, was trying to force an unoffending stranger to a fight.

My vanity was wounded, but I felt more sorry for her than for myself, and when she spoke again I listened eagerly, hoping she would say something which would soften what had gone before. But she did not make it easier for either of us.

" If I persuade my brother to apologize for what he said of your regiment," she continued, " will you accept his apology ? " Her tone was one partly of interrogation, partly of command. " I do not think he is likely to do so," she added, " but if you will let that suffice, I shall see him at once, and ask him."

" You need not do that ! " I replied, quickly. " As I have said, it is not my affair. It concerns my—a great many people. I am sorry, but the meeting must take place."

For the first time Miss Fiske smiled, but it was the same smile of amusement with which she had regarded us when she first saw us in the plaza.

" I quite understand," she said, still smiling. " You need not assure me that it concerns a great many people." She turned away as though the interview was at an end, and then halted. She had stepped into the circle of the moonlight so that her beauty shone full upon me.

" I know that it concerns a great many people," she cried. " I know that it is all a part of the plot against my father ! "

I gave a gasp of consternation which she misconstrued, for she continued, bitterly.

"Oh, I know everything," she said. "Mr. Graham has told me all that you mean to do. I was foolish to appeal to any one of you. You have set out to fight my father, and your friends will use any means to win. But I should have thought," she cried, her voice rising and ringing like an alarm, "that they would have stopped at assassinating his son."

I stepped back from her as though she had struck at me.

"Miss Fiske," I cried. What she had charged was so monstrous, so absurd that I could answer nothing in defence. My brain refused to believe that she had said it. I could not conceive that any creature so utterly lovely could be so unseeing, so bitter, and so unfair.

Her charge was ridiculous, but my disappointment in her was so keen that the tears came to my eyes.

I put my hat back on my head, saluted her and passed her quickly.

"Captain Macklin," she cried. "What is it? What have I said?" She stretched out her hand toward me, but I did not stop.

"Captain Macklin!" she called after me in such a voice that I was forced to halt and turn.

"What are you going to do?" she demanded. "Oh, yes, I see," she exclaimed. "I see how it sounded to you. And you?" she cried. Her voice was trembling with concern. "Because I said that, you mean to punish me for it—through my brother? You mean to make him suffer. You will kill him!" Her voice rose to an accent of terror. "But I only said it because he is my brother, my own brother. Cannot you understand what that means to me? Cannot you understand why I said it?"

We stood facing each other, I, staring at her miserably, and she breathing quickly, and holding her hand to her side as though she had been running a long distance.

"No," I said in a low voice. It was very hard for me to speak at all. "No, I cannot understand."

I pulled off my hat again, and stood before her crushing it in my hands.

"Why didn't you trust me?" I said, bitterly. "How could you doubt what I would do? I trusted you. From the moment you came riding toward me, I thanked God for the sight of such a woman. For making anything so beautiful."

I stopped, for I saw I had again offended. At the words she drew back quickly, and her eyes shone with indignation. She looked at me as though I had tried to touch her with my hand. But I spoke on without heeding her. I repeated the words with which I had offended.

"Yes," I said, "I thanked God for anything so noble and so beautiful. To me, you could do no wrong. But you! You judged me before you even knew my name. You said I was a cad who went about armed to fight unarmed men. To you I was a coward who could be frightened off by a tale of bulls-eyes, and broken pipe-stems at a Paris fair. What do I care for your brother's tricks. Let him see my score cards at West Point. He'll find them framed on the walls. I was first a coward and a cad, and now I am a bully and a hired assassin. From the first, you and your brother have laughed at me and mine while all I asked of you was to be what you seemed to be, what I was happy to think you were. I wanted to believe in you. Why did you show me that you can be selfish and unfeeling? It is you who do not understand. You understand so little," I cried, "that I pity you from the bottom of my heart. I give you my word, I pity you."

"Stop," she commanded. I drew back and bowed, and we stood confronting each other in silence.

"And they call you a brave man," she said at last, speaking slowly and steadily, as though she were picking each word. "It is like a brave man to insult a woman, because she wants to save her brother's life."

When I raised my face it was burning, as though she had thrown vitriol.

" If I have insulted you, Miss Fiske," I said, " if I have ever insulted any woman, I hope to God that to-morrow morning your brother will kill me."

When I turned and looked back at her from the door, she was leaning against one of the pillars with her face bent in her hands, and weeping bitterly.

I rode to the barracks and spent several hours in writing a long letter to Beatrice. I felt a great need to draw near to her. I was confused and sore and unhappy, and although nothing of this, nor of the duel appeared in my letter, I was comforted to think that I was writing it to her. It was good to remember that there was such a woman in the world, and when I compared her with the girl from whom I had just parted, I laughed out loud.

And yet I knew that had I put the case to Beatrice, she would have discovered something to present in favor of Miss Fiske.

" She was pleading for her brother, and she did not understand," Beatrice would have said. But in my own heart I could find no excuse. Her family had brought me nothing but evil. Because her father would not pay his debts, I had been twice wounded and many times had risked death; the son had struck me with a whip in the public streets, and the sister had called me everything that is contemptible, from a cad to a hired cut-throat. So, I was done with the house of Fiske. My hand was against it. I owed it nothing.

But with all my indignation against them, for which there was reason enough, I knew in my heart that I had looked up to them, and stood in awe of them, for reasons that made me the cad they called me. Ever since my arrival in Honduras I had been carried away by the talk of the Fiske millions, and later by the beauty of the girl, and by the boy's insolent air, of what I accepted as good breeding. I had been impressed with his five years in Paris, by the cut of his riding-clothes even, by the fact that he owned a yacht. I had looked up to them, because they belonged to a class who formed society, as I knew society through the Sunday papers. And now these superior beings had rewarded my snobbishness by acting toward me in a way that was contrary to every ideal I held of what was right and decent. For such as these, I had felt ashamed of my old comrades. It was humiliating, but it was true; and as I admitted this to myself, my cheeks burned in the darkness, and I buried my face in the pillow. For some time I lay awake debating fiercely in my mind as to whether, when I faced young Fiske, I should shoot the pistol out of his hand, or fire into the ground. And it was not until I had decided that the latter act would better show our contempt for him and his insult, that I fell asleep.

Von Ritter and Miller woke me at four o'clock. They were painfully correct and formal. Miller had even borrowed something of the Baron's manner, which sat upon him as awkwardly as would a wig and patches. I laughed at them both, but, for the time being, they had lost their sense of humor; and we drank our coffee in a constrained and sleepy silence.

At the graveyard we found that Fiske, his two seconds, Graham and Lowell, the young Middy, and a local surgeon had already arrived. We exchanged bows and salutes gloomily and the seconds gathered together, and began to talk in hoarse whispers. It was still very dark. The moon hung empty and pallid above the cold outline of the hills, and although the roosters were crowing cheerfully, the sun had not yet risen. In the hollows the mists lay like lakes, and every stone and rock was wet and shining as though it had been washed in readiness for the coming day. The gravestones shone upon us like freshly scrubbed doorsteps   It was a most dismal spot, and I was so cold that I was afraid I would shiver, and Fiske might think I was nervous. So I moved briskly about among the graves, reading the inscriptions on the tombstones. Under the circumstances the occupation, to a less healthy mind, would have been depressing. My adversary, so it seemed to me, carried himself with a little too much unconcern. It struck me that he overdid it. He laughed with the local surgeon, and pointed out the moon and the lakes of mist as though we had driven out to observe the view. I could not think of anything to do which would show that I was unconcerned too, so I got back into the carriage and stretched my feet out to the seat opposite, and continued to smoke my cigar.

Incidentally, by speaking to Lowell, I hurt Von Ritter's feelings. It seems that as one of the other man's seconds I should have been more haughty with him. But when he passed me, pacing out the ground, he saluted stiffly, and as I saluted back, I called out: "I suppose you know you'll catch it if they find out about this at Washington?" And he answered, with a grin: "Yes, I know, but I couldn't get out of it."

"Neither could I," I replied, cheerfully, and in so loud a tone that everyone heard me. Von Ritter was terribly annoyed.

Captain Macklin

At last all was arranged and we took our places. We were to use pistols. They were double-barrelled affairs, with very fine hair-triggers. Graham was to give the word by asking if we were ready, and was then to count "One, two, three."

After the word "one" we could fire when we pleased. When each of us had emptied both barrels, our honor was supposed to be satisfied.

Young Fiske wore a blue yachting suit with the collar turned up, and no white showing except his face, and that in the gray light of the dawn was a sickly white, like the belly of a fish. After he had walked to his mark he never took his eyes from me. They seemed to be probing around under my uniform for the vulnerable spot. I had never before had anyone look at me, who seemed to so frankly dislike me.

Curiously enough, I kept thinking of the story of the man who boasted he was so good a shot that he could break the stem of a wine-glass, and how someone said: "Yes, but the wine-glass isn't holding a pistol." Then, while I was smiling at the application I had made of this story to my scowling adversary, there came up a picture, not of home and of Beatrice, nor of my past sins, but of the fellow's sister as I last saw her in the moonlight, leaning against the pillar of the balcony with her head bowed in her hands. And at once it all seemed contemptible and cruel. No quarrel in the world, so it appeared to me then, was worth while if it were going to make a woman suffer. And for an instant I was so indignant with Fiske for having dragged me into this one, to feed his silly vanity, that for a moment I felt like walking over and giving him a sound thrashing. But at the instant I heard Graham demand, "Are you ready?" and I saw Fiske fasten his eyes on mine, and nod his head. The moment had come.

"One," Graham counted, and at the word Fiske threw up his gun and fired, and the ball whistled past my ear. My pistol was still hanging at my side, so I merely pulled the trigger, and the ball went into the ground. But instantly I saw my mistake. Shame and consternation were written on the faces of my two seconds, and to the face of Fiske there came a contemptuous smile. I at once understood my error. I read what was in the mind of each. They dared to think I had pulled the trigger through nervousness, that I had fired before I was ready, that I was frightened and afraid. I am sure I never was so angry in my life, and I would have cried out to them, if a movement on the part of Fiske had not sobered me. Still smiling, he lifted his pistol slightly and aimed for, so it seemed to me, some seconds, and then fired.

I felt the bullet cut the lining of my tunic and burn the flesh over my ribs, and the warm blood tickling my side, but I was determined he should not know he had hit me, and not even my lips moved.

Then a change, so sudden and so remarkable, came over the face of young Fiske, that its very agony fascinated me. At first it was incomprehensible, and then I understood. He had fired his last shot, he thought he had missed, and he was waiting for me, at my leisure, to kill him with my second bullet.

I raised the pistol, and it was as though you could hear the silence. Every waking thing about us seemed to suddenly grow still. I brought the barrel slowly to a level with his knee, raised it to his heart, passed it over his head, and, aiming in the air, fired at the moon, and then tossed the gun away. The waking world seemed to breathe again, and from every side there came a chorus of quick exclamations; but without turning to note who made them, nor what they signified, I walked back to the carriage, and picked up my cigar. It was still burning.

Von Ritter ran to the side of the carriage.

"You must wait," he protested. "Mr. Fiske wishes to shake hands with you. It is not finished yet."

"Yes, it is finished," I replied, savagely. "I have humored you two long enough. A pest on both your houses. I'm going back to breakfast."

Poor Von Ritter drew away, deeply hurt and scandalized, but my offence was nothing to the shock he received when young Lowell ran to the carriage and caught up my hand. He looked at me with a smile that would have softened a Spanish duenna.

"See here!" he cried. "Whether you like it or not, you've got to shake hands with me. I want to tell you that was one of the finest things I ever saw." He squeezed my fingers until the bones crunched together. "I've heard a lot about you, and now I believe all I've heard. To stand up there," he ran on, breathlessly, "knowing you didn't mean to fire, and knowing he was a dead shot, and make a canvas target of yourself—that was bully. You were an ass to do it, but it was great. You going back to breakfast?" he demanded, suddenly, with the same winning, eager smile. "So am I. I speak to go with you."

Before I could reply he had vaulted into the carriage, and was shouting at the driver.

" Cochero, to the Barracks. Full speed ahead. Vamoose. Give way. Allez vite ! "

" But my seconds," I protested.

" They can walk," he said.

Already the horses were at a gallop, and as we swung around the wall of the graveyard and were hidden from the sight of the others, Lowell sprang into the seat beside me. With the quick fingers of the sailor, he cast off my sword-belt and tore open my blouse.

" I wanted to get you away," he muttered, " before he found out he had hit you."

" I'm not hit," I protested.

" Just as you like," he said. " Still, it looks rather damp to the left here."

But, as I knew, the bullet had only grazed me, and the laugh of relief Lowell gave when he raised his head, and said, " Why, it's only a scratch," meant as much to me as though he had rendered me some great service. For it seemed to prove a genuine, friendly concern, and no one, except Laguerre, had shown that for me since I had left home. I had taken a fancy to Lowell from the moment he had saluted me like a brother officer in the Plaza, and I had wished he would like me. I liked him better than any other young man I had ever met. I had never had a man for a friend, but before we had finished breakfast I believe we were better friends than many boys who had lived next door to each other from the day they were babies.

As a rule, I do not hit it off with men, so I felt that his liking me was a great piece of good fortune, and a great honor. He was only three years older than myself, but he knew much more about everything than I did, and his views of things were as fine and honorable as they were amusing.

Since then we have grown to be very close friends indeed, and we have ventured together into many queer corners, but I have never ceased to admire him, and I have always found him the same — unconscious of himself and sufficient to himself. I mean that if he were presented to an Empress he would not be impressed, nor if he chatted with a bar-maid would he be familiar. He would just look at each of them with his grave blue eyes and think only of what she was saying, and not at all of what sort of an impression he was making, or what she thought of him. Aiken helped me a lot by making me try not to be like Aiken; Lowell helped me by making me wish to be like Lowell.

We had a very merry breakfast, and the fact that it was seven in the morning did not in the least interfere with our drinking each other's health in a quart of champagne. Nearly all of our officers came in while we were at breakfast to learn if I were still alive, and Lowell gave them most marvellous accounts of the affair, sometimes representing me as an idiot and sometimes as an heroic martyr.

They all asked him if he thought Fiske had sufficient influence at Washington to cause the Government to give him the use of the Raleigh against us, but he would only laugh and shake his head.

Later, to Laguerre, he talked earnestly on the same subject, and much to the point.

The news of the duel had reached the palace at eight o'clock, and the president at once started for the barracks.

We knew he was coming when we heard the people in the cafés shouting " Viva," as they always did when he appeared in public, and, though I was badly frightened as to what he would say to me, I ran to the door and turned out the guard to receive him.

He had put on one of the foreign uniforms he was entitled to wear—he did not seem to fancy the one I had designed—and as he rode across the Plaza I thought I had never seen a finer soldier. Lowell said he looked like a field marshal of the Second Empire. I was glad Lowell had come to the door with me, as he could now see for himself that my general was one for whom a man might be proud to fight a dozen duels.

The president gave his reins to an orderly and mounted the steps, touching his chapeau to the salute of guard and the shouting citizens, but his eyes were fixed sternly on me. I saw that he was deeply moved, and I wished fervently, now that it was too late, that I had told him of the street fight at the time, and not allowed him to hear of it from others. I feared the worst. I was prepared for any reproof, any punishment, even the loss of my commission, and I braced myself for his condemnation.

But when he reached the top step where I stood at salute, although I was inwardly quaking, he halted and his lips suddenly twisted, and the tears rushed to his eyes.

He tried to speak, but made only a choking, inarticulate sound, and then, with a quick gesture, before all the soldiers and all the people, he caught me in his arms.

"My boy," he whispered, "my boy! For you were lost," he murmured, "and have returned to me."

I heard Lowell running away, and the door of the guard-room banging behind him. I heard the cheers of the people who, it seems, already knew of the duel and understood the tableau on the barrack steps, but the thought that Laguerre cared for me even as a son made me deaf to everything, and my heart choked with happiness.

It passed in a moment, and in manner he was once more my superior officer, but the door he had opened was never again wholly shut to me.

In the guard-room I presented Lowell to the president, and I was proud to see the respect with which Lowell addressed him. At the first glance they seemed to understand each other, and they talked together as simply as would friends of long acquaintance.

After they had spoken of many things, La-guerre said: "Would it be fair for me to ask you, Mr. Lowell, what instructions the United States has given your commanding officer in regard to our government?"

To this Lowell answered: "All I know, sir, is that when we arrived at Amapala, Captain Miller telegraphed the late president, Doctor Alvarez, that we were here to protect American interests. But you probably know," he added, "as every-one else does, that we came here because the Isthmian Line demanded protection."

"Yes, so I supposed," Laguerre replied. "But I understand Mr. Graham has said that when Mr. Fiske gives the word Captain Miller will land your marines and drive us out of the country."

Lowell shrugged his shoulders and frowned.

" Mr. Graham—" he began, "is Mr. Graham." He added: " Captain Miller is not taking orders from civilians, and he depends on his own sources for information. I am here because he sent me to ' Go, look, see,' and report. I have been wiring him ever since you started from the coast, and since you became president. Your censor has very kindly allowed me to use our cipher."

I laughed, and said: " We court investigation."

" Pardon me, sir," Lowell answered, earnestly, addressing himself to Laguerre, " but I should think you would. Why," he exclaimed, " every merchant in the city has told me he considers his interests have never been so secure as since you became president. It is only the Isthmian Line that wants the protection of our ship. The foreign merchants are not afraid. I hate it!" he cried, " I hate to think that a billionaire, with a pull at Washington, can turn our Jackies into Janissaries. Protect American interests!" he exclaimed, indignantly, " protect American sharpers! The Isthmian Line has no more right to the protection of our Navy than have the debtors in Ludlow Street Jail."

Laguerre sat for a long time without replying, and then rose and bowed to Lowell with great courtesy.

"I must be returning," he said. "I thank you, sir, for your good opinion. At my earliest convenience I shall pay my respects to your commanding officer. At ten o'clock," he continued turning to me, "I am to have my talk with Mr. Fiske. I have not the least doubt but that he will see the justice of our claim against his company, and before evening I am sure I shall be able to announce throughout the republic that I have his guaranty for the money. Mr. Fiske is an able, upright business man, as well as a gentleman, and he will not see this country robbed."

He shook hands with us and we escorted him to his horse.

I always like to remember him as I saw him then, in that gorgeous uniform, riding away under the great palms of the Plaza, with the tropical sunshine touching his white hair, and flashing upon the sabres of the body-guard, and the people running from every side of the square to cheer him.

Two hours later, when I had finished my "paper" work and was setting forth on my daily round, Miller came galloping up to the barracks and flung himself out of the saddle. He nodded to Lowell, and pulled me roughly to one side.

"The talk with Fiske," he whispered, "ended in the deuce of a row. Fiske behaved like a mule. He told Laguerre that the original charter of the company had been tampered with, and that the one Laguerre submitted to him was a fake copy. And he ended by asking Laguerre to name his price to leave them alone."

"And Laguerre?"

"Well, what do you suppose," Miller returned, scornfully. "The General just looked at him, and then picked up a pen, and began to write, and said to the orderly, 'Show him out.'

"'What's that?' Fiske said. And Laguerre answered: 'Merely a figure of speech; what I really meant was "Put him out," or "throw him out!" You are an offensive and foolish old man. I, the President of this country, received you and conferred with you as one gentleman with another, and you tried to insult me. You are either extremely ignorant, or extremely dishonest, and I shall treat with you no longer. Instead, I shall at once seize every piece of property belonging to your company, and hold it until you pay your debts. Now you go, and congratulate yourself that when you tried to insult me, you did so when you were under my roof, at my invitation.'

Then Laguerre wired the commandantes at all the seaports to seize the warehouses and officers of the Isthmian Line, and even its ships, and to occupy the buildings with troops. He means business," Miller cried, jubilantly. "This time it's a fight to a finish."

Lowell had already sent for his horse, and altogether we started at a gallop for the palace. At the office of the Isthmian Line we were halted by a crowd so great that it blocked the street. The doors of the building were barred, and two sentries were standing guard in front of it. A proclamation on the wall announced that, by order of the President, the entire plant of the Isthmian Line had been confiscated, and that unless within two weeks the company paid its debts to the government, the government would sell the property of the company until it had obtained the money due it.

At the entrance to the palace the sergeant in charge of the native guard, who was one of our men, told us that two ships of the Isthmian Line had been caught in port; one at Cortez on her way to Aspinwall, and one at Truxillo, bound north. The passengers had been landed, and were to remain on shore as guests of the government until they could be transferred to another line.

Lowell's face as he heard this was very grave, and he shook his head.

"A perfectly just reprisal, if you ask me," he said, "but what one lonely ensign tells you in confidence, and what Fiske will tell the State Department at Washington, is a very different matter. It's a good thing," he exclaimed, with a laugh, "that the Raleigh's on the wrong side of the Isthmus. If we were in the Caribbean, they might order us to make you give back those ships. As it is, we can't get marines here from the Pacific under three days. So I'd better start them at once," he added, suddenly. "Good-by, I must wire the Captain."

"Don't let the United States Navy do anything reckless," I said. "I'm not so sure you could take those ships, and I'm not so sure your marines can get here in three days, either, or that they ever could get here."

Lowell gave a shout of derision.

"What," he cried, "you'd fight against your country's flag?"

I told him he must not forget that at West Point they had decided I was not good enough to fight for my country's flag.

"We've three ships of our own now," I added, with a grin. "How would you like to be Rear-Admiral of the naval forces of Honduras?"

Lowell caught up his reins in mock terror.

"What!" he cried. "You'd dare to bribe an American officer? And with such a fat bribe, too?" he exclaimed. "A Rear-Admiral at my age! That's dangerously near my price. I'm afraid to listen to you. Good-by." He waved his hand and started down the street. "Good-by, Satan," he called back to me, and I laughed, and he rode away.

That was the end of the laughter, of the jests, of the play-acting.

After that it was grim, grim, bitter and miserable. We dogs had had our day. We soldiers of either fortune had tasted our cup of triumph, and though it was only a taste, it had flown to our brains like heavy wine, and the headaches and the heartaches followed fast. For some it was more than a heartache; to them it brought the deep, drugged sleep of Nirvana.

The storm broke at the moment I turned from Lowell on the steps of the palace, and it did not cease, for even one brief breathing space, until we were cast forth, and scattered, and beaten.

As Lowell left me, General Laguerre, with Aiken at his side, came hurrying down the hall of the palace. The President was walking with his head bowed, listening to Aiken, who was whispering and gesticulating vehemently. I had never seen him so greatly excited. When he caught sight of me he ran forward.

"Here he is," he cried. "Have you heard from Heinze?" he demanded. "Has he asked you to send him a native regiment to Pecachua?"

"Yes," I answered, "he wanted natives to dig trenches. I sent five hundred at eight this morning."

Aiken clenched his fingers. It was like the quick, desperate clutch of a drowning man.

"I'm right," he cried. He turned upon Laguerre. "Macklin has sent them. By this time our men are prisoners."

Laguerre glanced sharply at the native guard drawn up at attention on either side of us. "Hush," he said. He ran past us down the steps, and halting when he reached the street, turned and looked up at the great bulk of El Pecachua that rose in the fierce sunlight, calm and inscrutable, against the white, glaring masses of the clouds.

"What is it?" I whispered.

"Heinze!" Aiken answered, savagely. "Heinze has sold them Pecachua."

I cried out, but again Laguerre commanded silence. "You do not know that," he said; but his voice trembled, and his face was drawn in lines of deep concern.

" I warned you ! " Aiken cried, roughly. " I warned you yesterday ; I told you to send Macklin to Pecachua."

He turned on me and held me by the sleeve, but like Laguerre he still continued to look fearfully toward the mountain.

"They came to me last night, Graham came to me," he whispered. " He offered me ten thousand dollars gold, and I did not take it." In his wonder at his own integrity, in spite of the excitement which shook him, Aiken's face for an instant lit with a weak, gratified smile. " I pretended to consider it," he went on, " and sent another of my men to Pecachua. He came back an hour ago. He tells me Graham offered Heinze twenty thousand dollars to buy off himself and the other officers and the men. But Heinze was afraid of the others, and so he planned to ask Laguerre for a native regiment, to pretend that he wanted them to work on the trenches. And then, when our men were lying about, suspecting nothing, the natives should fall on them and tie them, or shoot them, and then turn the guns on the city. And he *has* sent for the niggars !" Aiken cried. " And there's not one of them that wouldn't sell you out. They're there now !" he cried, shaking his hand at the mountain. " I warned you ! I warned you !"

Incredible as it seemed, difficult as it was to believe such baseness, I felt convinced that Aiken spoke the truth. The thought sickened me, but I stepped over to Laguerre and saluted.

"I can assemble the men in half an hour," I said. "We can reach the base of the rock an hour later."

"But if it should not be true," Laguerre protested. "The insult to Heinze——"

"Heinze!" Aiken shouted, and broke into a volley of curses. But the oaths died in his throat. We heard a whirr of galloping hoofs; a man's voice shrieking to his horse; the sounds of many people running, and one of my scouts swept into the street, and raced toward us. He fell off at our feet, and the pony rolled upon its head, its flanks heaving horribly and the blood spurting from its nostrils.

"Garcia and Alvarez!" the man panted. "They're making for the city. They tried to fool us. They left their tents up, and fires burning, and started at night, but I smelt 'em the moment they struck the trail. We fellows have been on their flanks since sun-up, picking 'em off at long range, but we can't hold them. They'll be here in two hours."

"Now, will you believe me?" Aiken shouted. "That's their plot. They're working together.

They mean to trap us on every side. Ah!" he cried. "Look!"

I knew the thing at which he wished me to look. His voice and my dread told me at what his arm was pointing.

I raised my eyes fearfully to El Pecachua. From its green crest a puff of smoke was swelling into a white cloud, the cloud was split with a flash of flame, and the dull echo of the report drifted toward us on the hot, motionless air. At the same instant our flag on the crest of Pecachua, the flag with the five-pointed, blood-red star, came twitching down; and a shell screeched and broke above us.

Now that he knew the worst, the doubt and concern on the face of General Laguerre fell from it like a mask.

"We have no guns that will reach the mountain, have we?" he asked. He spoke as calmly as though we were changing guard.

"No, not one," I answered. "All our heavy pieces are on Pecachua."

"Then we must take it by assault," he said. "We will first drive Garcia back, and then we will storm the hill, or starve them out. Assemble all the men at the palace at once. Trust to no one but yourself. Ride to every outpost and order them here. Send Von Ritter and the gatlings to meet Alvarez. This man will act as his guide."

He turned to the scout. "You will find my horse in the court-yard of the palace," he said to him. "Take it, and accompany Captain Macklin. Tell Von Ritter," he continued, turning to me, "not to expose his men, but to harass the enemy, and hold him until I come." His tone was easy, confident, and assured. Even as I listened to his command I marvelled at the rapidity with which his mind worked, how he rose to an unexpected situation, and met unforeseen difficulties.

"That is all," he said. "I will expect the men here in half an hour."

He turned from me calmly. As he re-entered the palace between the lines of the guard he saluted as punctiliously as though he were on his way to luncheon.

But no one else shared in his calmness. The bursting shells had driven the people from their houses, and they were screaming through the streets, as though an earthquake had shaken the city. Even the palace was in an uproar.

The scout, as he entered it, shouting for the President's horse, had told the story to our men, and they came running to the great doors, fastening their accoutrements as they ran. Outside, even as Laguerre had been speaking, the people had gathered in a great circle, whispering and gesticulating, pointing at us, at the dying horse, at the shells that swung above us, at the flag of Alvarez which floated from Pecachua. When I spurred my horse forward, with the scout at my side, there was a sullen silence. The smiles, the raised hats, the cheers were missing, and I had but turned my back on them when a voice shouted, "Viva Alvarez!"

I swung in my saddle, and pulled out my sword. I thought it was only the bravado of some impudent fellow who needed a lesson.

But it was a signal, for as I turned I saw the native guard spring like one man upon our sergeant and drive their bayonets into his throat. He went down with a dozen of the dwarf-like negroes stabbing and kicking at him, and the mob ran shrieking upon the door of the palace.

On the instant I forgot everything except Laguerre. I had only one thought, to get to him, to place myself at his side.

I pushed my horse among the people, beating at the little beasts with my sword. But the voice I knew best of all called my name from just above my head, and I looked up and saw Laguerre with Aiken and Webster on the iron balcony of the palace.

Laguerre's face was white and set.

"Captain Macklin!" he cried. "What does this mean? Obey your orders. You have my orders. Obey my orders."

"I can't," I cried. "This is an attack upon you! They will kill you!"

At the moment I spoke our men fired a scattering volley at the mob, and swung to the great gates. The mob answered their volley with a dozen pistol-shots, and threw itself forward. Still looking up, I saw Laguerre clasp his hands to his throat, and fall back upon Webster's shoulder, but he again instantly stood upright and motioned me fiercely with his arm. "Go," he cried. "Bring the gatlings here, and all the men. If you delay we lose the palace. Obey my orders," he again commanded, with a second fierce gesture.

The movement was all but fatal. The wound in his throat tore apart, his head fell forward and his eyes closed. I saw the blood spreading and dyeing the gold braid. But he straightened himself and leaned forward. His eyes opened, and, holding himself erect with one hand on the railing of the balcony, he stretched the other over me, as though in benediction.

"Go, Royal!" he cried, "and—God bless you!"

VI

I BENT my head and drove my spurs into my horse. I did not know where he was carrying me. My eyes were shut with tears, and with the horror of what I had witnessed. I was reckless, mad, for the first time in my life, filled with hate against my fellow-men. I rode a hundred yards before I heard the scout at my side shouting, " To the right, Captain, to the right."

At the word I pulled on my rein, and we turned into the Plaza.

The scout was McGraw, the Kansas cowboy, who had halted Aiken and myself the day we first met with the filibusters. He was shooting from the saddle as steadily as other men would shoot with a rest, and each time he fired, he laughed. The laugh brought me back to the desperate need of our mission. I tricked myself into believing that Laguerre was not seriously wounded. I persuaded myself that by bringing him aid quickly I was rendering him as good service as I might have given had I remained at his side. I shut out the picture of him, faint and bleeding, and opened my eyes to the work before us.

We were like the lost dogs on a race-course

that run between lines of hooting men. On every side we were assailed with cries. Even the voices of women mocked at us. Men sprang at my bridle, and my horse rode them down. They shot at us from the doors of the cafés, from either curbstone. As we passed the barracks even the men of my own native regiment raised their rifles and fired.

The nearest gun was at the end of the Calle Bogran, and we raced down it, each with his revolver cocked, and held in front of him.

But before we reached the outpost I saw the men who formed it, pushing their way toward us, bunched about their gatling with their clubbed rifles warding off the blows of a mob that struck at them from every side. They were ignorant of what had transpired; they did not know who was, or who was not their official enemy, and they were unwilling to fire upon the people, who a moment before, before the flag of Alvarez had risen on Pecachua, had been their friends and comrades. These friends now beset them like a pack of wolves. They hung upon their flanks and stabbed at them from the front and rear. The air was filled with broken tiles from the roofs, and with flying paving-stones.

When the men saw us they raised a broken cheer.

Captain Macklin

"Open that gun on them!" I shouted. "Clear the street, and push your gun to the palace. Laguerre is there. Kill every man in this street if you have to, but get to the palace."

The officer in charge fought his way to my side. He was covered with sweat and blood. He made a path for himself with his bare arms.

"What in hell does this mean, Macklin?" he shouted. "Who are we fighting?"

"You are fighting every native you see," I ordered. "Let loose up this street. Get to the palace!"

I rode on to the rear of the gun, and as McGraw and I raced on toward the next post, we heard it stabbing the air with short, vicious blows.

At the same instant the heavens shook with a clap of thunder, the sky turned black, and with the sudden fierceness of the tropics, heavy drops of rain began to beat upon us, and to splash in the dust like hail.

A moment later and the storm burst upon the city. The streets were swept with great sheets of water, torrents flowed from the housetop, the skies darkened to ink, or were ripped asunder by vivid flashes, and the thunder rolled unceasingly. We were half drowned, as though we were dragged through a pond, and our ponies bowed and staggered before the double onslaught of wind and water. We bent our bodies to theirs, and lashed them forward.

The outpost to which we were now riding was stationed at the edge of the city where the Calle Morizan joins the trail to San Lorenzo on the Pacific coast. As we approached it I saw a number of mounted men, surrounding a closed carriage. They were evidently travellers starting forth on the three days' ride to San Lorenzo, to cross to Amapala, where the Pacific Mail takes on her passengers. They had been halted by our sentries. As I came nearer I recognized, through the mist of rain, Joseph Fiske, young Fiske, and a group of the Isthmian men. The storm, or the bursting shells, had stampeded their pack-train, and a dozen frantic Mozos were rounding up the mules and adding their shrieks and the sound of their falling whips to the tumult of the storm.

I galloped past them to where our main guard were lashing the canvas-cover to their gun, and ordered them to unstrap it, and fight their way to the palace.

As I turned again the sentry called : " Am I to let these people go ? They have no passes."

I halted, and Joseph Fiske raised his heavy eyelids, and blinked at me like a huge crocodile.

I put a restraint upon myself and moved toward him with a confident smile. I could not bear to have him depart, thinking he went in triumph. I looked the group over carefully and said : " Certainly, let them pass," and Fiske and some of the Isthmian men, who appeared ashamed, nodded at me sheepishly.

But one of them, who was hidden by the carriage, called out : " You'd better come, too ; your ship of state is getting water-logged."

I made no sign that I heard him, but McGraw instantly answered, " Yes, it looks so. The rats are leaving it ! "

At that the man called back tauntingly the old Spanish proverb : " He who takes Pecachua, sleeps in the palace." McGraw did not understand Spanish, and looked at me appealingly, and I retorted, " We've altered that, sir. The man who sleeps in the palace will take Pecachua to-night."

And McGraw added : " Yes, and he won't take it with thirty pieces of silver, either."

I started away, beckoning to McGraw, but, as we moved, Mr. Fiske pushed his pony forward.

" Can you give me a pass, sir? " he asked. He shouted the words, for the roaring of the storm drowned all ordinary sounds. " In case I meet with more of your men, can you give me a written pass?"

I knew that the only men of ours still outside of the city were a few scouts, but I could not let Fiske suspect that, so I whipped out my note-book and wrote:

"To commanders of all military posts: Pass bearer, Joseph Fiske, his family, servants, and baggage-train.

"ROYAL MACKLIN,
"*Vice-President of Honduras.*"

I tore out the page and gave it him, and he read it carefully and bowed.

"Does this include my friends?" he asked, nodding toward the Isthmian men.

"You can pass them off as your servants," I answered, and he smiled grimly.

The men had formed around the gun, and it was being pushed toward me, but as I turned to meet it I was again halted, this time by young Fiske, who rode his horse in front of mine, and held out his hand.

"You must shake hands with me!" he cried. "I acted like a cad." He bent forward, raising his other arm to shield his face from the storm. "I say, I acted like a cad," he shouted, "and I ask your pardon."

Captain Macklin

I took his hand and nodded. At the same moment as we held each other's hands the window of the carriage was pushed down and his sister leaned out and beckoned to me. Her face, beaten by the rain, and with her hair blown across it, was filled with distress.

"I want to thank you," she cried. "Thank you," she repeated, "for my brother. I thank you. I wanted you to know."

She stretched out her hand and I took it, and released it instantly, and as she withdrew her face from the window of the carriage, I dug my spurs into my pony and galloped on with the gun.

What followed is all confused.

I remember that we reached the third and last post just after the men had abandoned it, but that we overtook them, and with them fought our way through the streets. But through what streets, or how long it took us to reach the palace I do not know. No one thing is very clear to me. Even the day after, I remembered it only as a bad dream, in which I saw innumerable, dark-skinned faces pressing upon me with open mouths, and white eyeballs; lit by gleams of lightning and flashes of powder. I remember going down under my pony and thinking how cool and pleasant it was in the wet mud, and of being thrown back on him again as though I were a pack-saddle, and I remember wiping the rain out of my eyes with a wet sleeve, and finding the sleeve warm with blood. And then there was a pitchy blackness through which I kept striking at faces that sprang out of the storm, faces that when they were beaten down were replaced by other faces; drunken, savage, exulting. I remember the ceaseless booming of the thunder that shook the houses like an earthquake, the futile popping of revolvers, the whining shells overhead, the cries and groans, the Spanish oaths, and the heavy breathing of my men about me, and always just in front of us, the breathless whir of the gatling.

After that the next I remember I was inside the palace, and breaking holes in the wall with an axe. Some of my men took the axe from me, and said: "He's crazy, clean crazy," and Van Ritter and Miller fought with me, and held me down upon a cot. From the cot I watched the others making more holes in the wall, through which they shoved their rifles and then there was a great cheer outside, and a man came running in crying, "Alvarez and Heinze are at the corner with the twelve-pounders!" Then our men cursed like fiends, and swept out of the room, and as no one remained to hold me down, I stumbled after them into the big reception-hall, and came upon Laguerre, lying rigid and still upon a red-silk sofa. I thought he was dead, and screamed, and at that they seized me again and hustled me back to the cot, telling me that he was not dead, but that at any moment he might die, and that if I did not rest, I would die also.

When I came to, it was early morning, and through the holes in the plaster wall I could see the stars fading before the dawn. The gatlings were gone and the men were gone, and I was wondering if they had deserted me, when Von Ritter came back and asked if I were strong enough to ride, and I stood up feeling dizzy and very weak. But my head was clear and I could understand what he said to me. Of the whole of the Foreign Legion only thirty were left. Miller was killed, Russell was killed and old man Webster was killed. They told me how they had caught him when he made a dash to the barracks for ammunition, and how, from the roof, our men had seen them place him against the iron railings of the University Gardens. There he died, as his hero, William Walker, had died, on the soil of the country he had tried to save from itself, with his arms behind him, and his blindfolded eyes turned upon a firing-squad.

McGraw had been killed as he rode beside me, holding me in the saddle. That hurt me worse than all. They told me a blow from behind had knocked me over, and though, of that, I could remember nothing, I could still feel McGraw's arm pressing my ribs, and hear his great foolish laugh in my ears.

They helped me out into the court-yard, where the men stood in a hollow square, with Laguerre on a litter in the centre, and with the four gatlings at each corner. The wound was in his throat, so he could not speak, but when they led me down into the Patio he raised his eyes and smiled. I tried to smile back, but his face was so white and drawn that I had to turn away, that he might not see me crying.

There was much besides to make one weep. We were running away. We were abandoning the country to which some of us had come to better their fortunes, to which others had come that they might set the people free. We were being driven out of it by the very men for whom we had risked our lives. Some among us, the reckless, the mercenary, the adventurers, had played like gamblers for a stake, and had lost. Others, as they thought, had planned wisely for the people's good, had asked nothing in return but that they might teach them to rule themselves. But they, too, had lost, and because they had lost, they were to pay the penalty.

Within the week the natives had turned from us to the painted idols of their jungle, and the new gods toward whom they had wavered were to be sacrificed on the altars of the old. They were waiting only until the sun rose to fall upon our little garrison and set us up against the barrack wall, as a peace offering to their former masters. Only one chance remained to us. If, while it were still night, we could escape from the city to the hills, we might be able to fight our way to the Pacific side, and there claim the protection of our war-ship.

It was a forlorn hope, but we trusted to the gatlings to clear a road for us, and there was no other way.

So just before the dawn, silently and stealthily the President and the Cabinet, and all that was left of the Government and Army of General Laguerre, stole out of his palace through a hole in the courtyard-wall.

We were only a shadowy blot in the darkness, but the instant we reached the open street they saw us and gave cry.

From behind the barriers they had raised to shut off our escape, from the house-tops, and from the darkened windows, they opened fire with rifle and artillery. But our men had seen the dead faces of their leaders and comrades, and they were frantic, desperate. They charged like madmen. Nothing could hold them. Our wedge swept steadily forward, and the guns sputtered from the front and rear and sides, flashing and illuminating the night like a war-ship in action.

They drove our enemies from behind the barricades, and cleaned the street beyond it to the bridge, and then swept the bridge itself. We could hear the splashes when the men who held it leaped out of range of the whirling bullets into the stream below.

In a quarter of an hour we were running swiftly through the sleeping suburbs, with only one of our guns barking an occasional warning at the ghostly figures in our rear.

We made desperate progress during the dark hours of the morning, but when daylight came we were afraid to remain longer on the trail, and turned off into the forest. And then, as the sun grew stronger, our endurance reached its limit, and when they called a halt our fellows dropped where they stood, and slept like dead men. But they could not sleep for long. We all knew that our only chance lay in reaching San Lorenzo, on the Pacific Ocean. Once there, we were confident that the war-ship would protect us, and her surgeons save our wounded. By the trail and unmolested, we could have reached it in three days, but in the jungle we were forced to cut our way painfully and slowly, and at times we did not know whether we were moving toward the ocean or had turned back upon the capital.

I do not believe that slaves hunted through a swamp by blood-hounds have ever suffered more keenly than did the survivors of the Foreign Legion. Of our thirty men, only five were unwounded. Even those who carried Laguerre wore blood-stained bandages. All were starving, and after the second day of hiding in swamps and fording mountain-streams, half of our little band was sick with fever. We lived on what we found in the woods, or stole from the clearing, on plants, and roots, and fruit. We were no longer a military body. We had ceased to be either officers or privates. We were now only so many wretched fellow-beings, dependent upon each other, like sailors cast adrift upon some desert island, and each worked for the good of all, and the ties which bound us together were stronger than those of authority and discipline. Men scarcely able to drag themselves on, begged for the privilege of helping to carry Laguerre, and he in turn besought and commanded that we leave him by the trail, and hasten to the safety of the coast. In one of his conscious moments he protested: "I cannot live, and I am only hindering your escape. It is not right, nor human, that one man should risk the lives of all the rest. For God's sake, obey my orders and put me down."

Hour after hour, by night as well as by day, we struggled forward, staggering, stumbling, some raving with fever, others with set faces, biting their yellow lips to choke back the pain.

Three times when we endeavored to gain ground by venturing on the level trail, the mounted scouts of Alvarez overtook us, or attacked us from ambush, and when we beat them off, they rode ahead and warned the villages that we were coming; so, that, when we reached them, we were driven forth like lepers. Even the village dogs snapped and bit at the gaunt figures, trembling for lack of food, and loss of sleep and blood.

But on the sixth day, just at sunset, as we had dragged ourselves to the top of a wooded hill we saw below us, beyond a league of unbroken jungle, a great, shining sheet of water, like a cloud on the horizon, and someone cried: "The Pacific!" and we all stumbled forward, and some dropped on their knees, and some wept, and some swung their hats and tried to cheer.

And then one of them, I never knew which, started singing, "Praise God, from whom all blessings flow," and we stood up, the last of the Legion, shaken with fever, starving, wounded, and hunted by our fellow-men, and gave praise to God, as we had never praised Him before.

That night the fever took hold of me, and in my tossings and turnings I burst open the sword-wound at the back of my head. I remember someone exclaiming " He's bled to death ! " and a torch held to my eyes, and then darkness, and the sense that I was being carried and bumped about on men's shoulders.

The next thing I knew I was lying in a hammock, a lot of naked, brown children were playing in the dirt beside me, the sun was shining, great palms were bending in the wind above me, and the strong, sweet air of the salt sea was blowing in my face.

I lay for a long time trying to guess where I was, and how I had come there. But I found no explanation for it, so I gave up guessing, and gazed contentedly at the bending palms until one of the children found my eyes upon him, and gave a scream, and they all pattered off like frightened partridges.

That brought a native woman from behind me, smiling, and murmuring prayers in Spanish. She handed me a gourd filled with water.

I asked where I was, and she said, " San Lorenzo."

I could have jumped out of the hammock at

that, but when I tried to do so I found I could hardly raise my body. But I had gained the coast. I knew I would find strength enough to leave it.

"Where are my friends?" I asked. "Where are the Gringoes?"

But she raised her hands, and threw them wide apart.

"They have gone," she said, "three, four days from now, they sailed away in the white ship. There was a great fighting," she said, raising her eyes and shaking her head, "and they carried you here, and told me to hide you. You have been very ill, and you are still very ill." She gave a little exclamation and disappeared, and returned at once with a piece of folded paper. "For you," she said.

On the outside of the paper was written in Spanish: "This paper will be found on the body of Royal Macklin. Let the priest bury him and send word to the Military Academy, West Point, U. S. A., asking that his family be informed of his place of burial. They will reward you well."

Inside, in English, was the following letter in Aiken's handwriting:

"DEAR OLD MAN—We had to drop you here, as we were too sick to carry you any farther. They jumped us at San Lorenzo, and when we found we couldn't get to Anapala from here, we decided to scatter, and let each man take care of himself. Von Ritter and I, and two of the boys, are taking Laguerre with us. He is still alive, but very bad. We hope to pick up a fishing-boat outside of town, and make for the Raleigh. We tried to carry you, too, but it wasn't possible. We had to desert one of you, so we stuck by the old man. We hid your revolver and money-belt under the seventh palm, on the beach to the right of this shack. If I'd known you had twenty double eagles on you all this time, I'd have cracked your skull myself. The crack you've got is healing, and if you pull through the fever you'll be all right. If you do, give this woman twenty pesos I borrowed from her. Get her to hire a boat, and men, and row it to Amapala. This island is only fifteen miles out, and the Pacific Mail boat touches there Thursdays and Sundays. If you leave here the night before, you can make it. Whatever you do, don't go into the village here or land at Amapala. If they catch you on shore they will surely shoot you. So board the steamer in the offing. Hoping you will live to read this, and that we may meet again under more agreeable circumstances, I am,

"Yours truly,

"HERBERT AIKEN."

" P.S.   I have your gilt sword, and I'm going to
turn it over to the officers of the Raleigh, to take
back to your folks.   Good luck to you, old man."

After reading this letter, which I have pre-
served carefully as a characteristic souvenir of
Aiken, I had but two anxieties.   The first was to
learn if Laguerre and the others had reached the
Raleigh, and the second was how could I escape
to the steamer—the first question was at once
answered by the woman.   She told me it was
known in San Lorenzo that the late " Presidente
Generale," with three Gringoes, had reached the
American war-ship and had been received on board.
The Commandante of Amapala had demanded
their surrender to him, but the captain of the ship
had declared that as political refugees, they were
entitled to the protection they claimed, and when
three days later he had been ordered to return to
San Francisco, he had taken them with him.

When I heard that, I gave a cheer all by myself, and I felt so much better for the news that
I at once began to plot for my own departure.
The day was Wednesday, the day before the
steamer left Amapala, and I determined to start
for the island the following evening.   When I
told the woman this, she protested I was much
too weak to move, but the risk that my hiding-

place might be discovered before another steamer-day arrived was much too great, and I insisted on making a try for the first one.

The woman accordingly procured a fishing-boat and a crew of three men, and I dug up my money-belt, and my revolver, and thanked her and paid her, for Aiken and for myself, as well as one can pay a person for saving one's life. The next night, as soon as the sun set, I seated myself in the stern of the boat, and we pushed out from the shore of Honduras, and were soon rising and falling on the broad swell of the Pacific.

My crew were simple fishermen, unconcerned with politics, and as I had no fear of harm from them, I curled up on a mat at their feet and instantly fell asleep.

When I again awoke the sun was well up, and when I raised my head the boatman pointed to a fringe of palms that hung above the water, and which he told me rose from the Island of Ama-pala. Two hours later we made out the wharves and the custom-house of the port itself, and, lying well toward us in the harbor, a big steamer with the smoke issuing from her stacks, and the American flag hanging at the stern. I was still weak and shaky, and I must confess that I choked a bit at the sight of the flag, and at the thought that, in spite of all, I was going safely back to life, and Beatrice and Aunt Mary. The name I made out on the stern of the steamer was Barracouta, and I considered it the prettiest name I had ever known, and the steamer the handsomest ship that ever sailed the sea. I loved her from her keel to her topmast. I loved her every line and curve, her every rope and bolt. But specially did I love the flag at her stern and the blue Peter at the fore. They meant home. They meant peace, friends, and my own countrymen.

I gave the boatmen a double eagle, and we all shook hands with great glee, and then with new strength and unassisted I pulled myself up the companion-ladder, and stood upon the deck.

When I reached it I wanted to embrace the first man I saw. I somehow expected that he would want to embrace me, too, and say how glad he was I had escaped. But he happened to be the ship's purser, and, instead of embracing me, he told me coldly that steerage passengers are not allowed aft. But I did not mind, I knew that I was a disreputable object, but I also knew that I had gold in my money-belt, and that clothes could be bought from the slop-chest.

So I said in great good-humor, that I wanted a first-class cabin, the immediate use of the bath-room, and the services of the ship's barber.

My head was bound in a dirty bandage. My

uniform, which I still wore as I had nothing else, was in rags from the briers, and the mud of the swamps and the sweat of the fever had caked it with dirt. I had an eight days' beard, and my bare feet were in native sandals. So my feelings were not greatly hurt because the purser was not as genuinely glad to see me as I was to see him.

" A first-class passage costs forty dollars gold —in advance," he said.

" That's all right," I answered, and I laughed from sheer, foolish happiness, " I'll take six."

We had been standing at the head of the companion-ladder, and as the purser moved rather reluctantly toward his cabin, a group of men came down the deck toward us.

One of them was a fat, red-faced American, the others wore the uniform of Alvarez. When they saw me they gave little squeals of excitement, and fell upon the fat man gesticulating violently, and pointing angrily at me.

The purser halted, and if it were possible, regarded me with even greater unfriendliness. As for myself, the sight of the brown, impish faces, and the familiar uniforms filled me with disgust. I had thought I was done with brawling and fighting, of being hated and hunted. I had had my fill of it. I wanted to be let alone, I wanted to feel that everybody about me was a friend. I was not in the least alarmed, for now that I was under the Stars and Stripes, I knew that I was immune from capture, but the mere possibility of a row was intolerable.

One of the Honduranians wore the uniform of a colonel, and was, as I guessed, the Commandante of the port. He spoke to the fat man in English, but in the same breath turned to one of his lieutenants, and gave an order in Spanish.

The lieutenant started in my direction, and then hesitated and beckoned to some one behind me.

I heard a patter of bare feet on the deck, and a dozen soldiers ran past me, and surrounded us. I noted that they and their officers belonged to the Eleventh Infantry. It was the regiment I had driven out of the barracks at Santa Barbara.

The fat American in his shirt-sleeves was listening to what the Commandante was saying, and apparently with great dissatisfaction. As he listened he scowled at me, chewing savagely on an unlit cigar, and rocking himself to and fro on his heels and toes. His thumbs were stuck in his suspenders, so that it looked as though, with great indecision he was pulling himself forward and back.

I turned to the purser and said, as carelessly as I could · " Well, what are we waiting for ? "

But he only shook his head.

With a gesture of impatience the fat man turned suddenly from the Commandante and came toward me.

He spoke abruptly and with the tone of a man holding authority.

"Have you got your police-permit to leave Amapala?" he demanded.

"No," I answered.

"Well, why haven't you?" he snapped.

"I didn't know I had to have one," I said. "Why do you ask?" I added. "Are you the captain of this ship?"

"I think I am," he suddenly roared, as though I had questioned his word. "Anyway, I've got enough say on her to put you ashore if you don't answer my questions."

I shut my lips together and looked away from him. His tone stirred what little blood there was still left in me to rebellion; but when I saw the shore with its swamps and ragged palms, I felt how perilously near it was, and Panama became suddenly a distant mirage. I was as helpless as a sailor clinging to a plank. I felt I was in no position to take offence, so I bit my lips and tried to smile.

The Captain shook his head at me, as though I were a prisoner in the dock.

" Do you mean to say," he shouted, " that our agent sold you a ticket without you showing a police-permit ? "

" I haven't got a ticket," I said. " I was just going to buy one now."

The Commandante thrust himself between us.

" Ah, what did I tell you ? " he cried. " You see ? He is escaping. This is the man. He answers all the descriptions. He was dressed just so ; green coat, red trousers, very torn and dirty—head in bandage. This is the description. Is it not so ? " he demanded of his lieutenants. They nodded vigorously.

" Why—a-yes, that is the man," the Commandante cried in triumph. " Last night he stabbed José Mendez in the Libertad Billiard Hall. He has wanted to murder him. If José, he die, this man he is murderer. He cannot go. He must come to land with me."

He gave an order in Spanish, and the soldiers closed in around us.

I saw that I was in great peril, in danger more real than any I had faced in open fight since I had entered Honduras. For the men who had met me then had fought with fair weapons. These men were trying to take away my life with a trick, with cunning lies and false witnesses.

They knew the Captain might not surrender a

passenger who was only a political offender, but that he could not harbor a criminal. And at the first glance at my uniform, and when he knew nothing more of me than that I wore it, the Commandante had trumped up this charge of crime, and had fitted to my appearance the imaginary description of an imaginary murderer. And I knew that he did this that he might send me, bound hand and foot, as a gift to Alvarez, or that he might, for his own vengeance, shoot me against a wall.

I knew how little I would receive of either justice or mercy. I had heard of Dr. Rojas killed between decks on a steamer of this same line; of Bonilla taken from the Ariadne and murdered on this very wharf at this very port of Amapala; of General Pulido strangled in the launch of the Commandante of Corinto and thrown overboard, while still in the sight of his fellow-passengers on the Southern Cross.

It was a degraded, horrible, inglorious end— to be caught by the heels after the real battle was lost; to die of fever in a cell; to be stabbed with bayonets on the wharf, and thrown to the carrion harbor-sharks.

I swung around upon the Captain, and fought for my life as desperately as though I had a rope around my neck.

"That man is a liar," I cried. "I was not in Amapala last night. I came from San Lorenzo this morning. The boat is alongside now; you can ask the men who brought me. I'm no murderer. That man knows I'm no murderer. He wants me because I belonged to the opposition government. It's because I wear this uniform he wants me. I'm no criminal. He has no more right to touch me here, than he would if I were on Broadway."

The Commandante seized the Captain's arm.

"As Commandante of this port," he screamed, "I tell you if you do not surrender the murderer to me, your ship shall not sail. I will take back your clearance-papers."

The Captain turned on me, shaking his red fists, and tossing his head like a bull. "You see that!" he cried. "You see what you get me into, coming on board my ship without a permit! That's what I get at every banana-patch along this coast, a lot of damned beach-combers and stowaways stealing on board, and the Commandante chasing 'em all over my ship and holding up my papers. You go ashore!" he ordered. He swept his arm toward the gangway. "You go to Kessler, our consul. If you haven't done nothing wrong, he'll take care of you. You haven't got a ticket, and you haven't got a permit, and you're no passenger of mine! Over you go; do you hear me? Quick now, over you go."

I could not believe that I heard the man aright. He seemed to be talking a language I did not know.

"Do you mean to tell me," I cried, speaking very slowly, for I was incredulous, and I was so weak besides that it was difficult for me to find the words, "that you refuse to protect me from these half-breeds, that you are going to turn me over to them—to be shot! And you call yourself an American?" I cried, "and this an American ship!"

As I turned from him I found that the passengers had come forward and now surrounded us; big, tall men in cool, clean linen, and beautiful women, shading their eyes with their fans, and little children crowding in between them and clinging to their skirts. To my famished eyes they looked like angels out of Paradise. They were my own people, and they brought back to me how I loved the life these men were plotting to take from me. The sight of them drove me into a sort of frenzy.

"Are you going to take that man's word against mine?" I cried at the Captain. "Are you going to let him murder me in sight of that flag? You know he'll do it. You know what they did to Rojas on one of your own ships. Do you want another man butchered in sight of your passengers?"

The Commandante crowded in front of the ship's captain.

"That man is my prisoner," he cried. "He is going to jail, to be tried by law. He shall see his consul every day. And so, if you try to leave this harbor with him, I will sink your ship from the fort!"

The Captain turned with an oath and looked up to the second officer, who was leaning over the rail of the bridge above us.

"Up anchor," the Captain shouted. "Get her under weigh! There is your answer," he cried, turning upon me. "I'm not going to have this ship held up any longer, and I'm not going to risk the lives of these ladies and gentlemen by any bombardment, either. You're only going to jail. I'll report the matter to our consul at Corinto, and he'll tell our minister."

"Corinto!" I replied. "I'll be dead before you've passed that lighthouse."

The Captain roared with anger.

"Can't you hear what he says," he shouted. "He says he'll fire on my ship. They've fired on our ships before! I'm not here to protect every damned scalawag that tries to stowaway on my ship. I'm here to protect the owners, and I mean to do it. Now you get down that ladder, before we throw you down."

I knew his words were final. From the bow I heard the creak of the anchor-chains as they were drawn on board, and from the engine-room the tinkle of bells.

The ship was abandoning me. My last appeal had failed. My condition was desperate.

"Protect your owners, and yourself, damn you!" I cried. "You're no American. You're no white man. No American would let a conchnigger run his ship. To hell with your protection!"

All the misery of the last two months, the bitterness of my dismissal from the Point, the ignominy of our defeat and flight, rose in me and drove me on. "And I don't want the protection of that flag either," I cried. "I wasn't good enough to serve it once, and I don't need it now."

It should be remembered that when I spoke these words I thought my death was inevitable and immediate, that it had been brought upon me by one of my own countrymen, while others of my countrymen stood indifferently by, and I hope that for what I said in that moment of fever and despair I may be forgiven.

" 1 can protect myself ! " I cried.

Before anyone could move I whipped out my gun and held it over the Commandante's heart, and at the same instant without turning my eyes from his face I waved my other hand at the passengers. " Take those children away," I shouted.

" Don't move ! " I yelled in Spanish at the soldiers. " If one of you raises his musket I'll kill him." I pressed the cocked revolver against the Commandante's chest. " Now, then, take me ashore," I called to his men. " You know me, I'm Captain Macklin. Captain Macklin, of the Foreign Legion, and you know that six of you will die before you get me. Come on," I taunted. " Which six is it to be ? "

Out of the corners of my eyes I could see the bayonets lifting cautiously and forming a ring of points about me, and the sight, and my own words lashed me into a frenzy of bravado.

" Oh, you don't remember me, don't you ? " I cried. " You ought to remember the Foreign Legion ! We drove you out of Santa Barbara and Tabla Ve and Comyagua, and I'm your Vice-President ! Take off your hats to your Vice-President ! To Captain Macklin, Vice-President of Honduras ! "

I sprang back against the cabin and swung

I sprang back against the cabin

the gun in swift half-circles. The men shrank from it as though I had lashed them with a whip. "Come on," I cried, "which six is it to be? Come on, you cowards, why don't you take me!"

The only answer came from a voice that was suddenly uplifted at my side. I recognized it as the voice of the ship's captain.

"Put down that gun!" he shouted.

But I only swung it the further until it covered him also. The man stood in terror of his ship's owners, he had a seaman's dread of international law, but he certainly was not afraid of a gun. He regarded it no more than a pointed finger, and leaned eagerly toward me. To my amazement I saw that his face was beaming with excitement and delight.

"Are you Captain Macklin?" he cried.

I was so amazed that for a moment I could only gape at him while I still covered him with the revolver.

"Yes," I answered.

"Then why in hell didn't you say so!" he roared, and with a bellow like a bull he threw himself upon the Commandante. He seized him by his epaulettes and pushed him backward. With the strength of a bull he butted and shoved him across the deck.

Captain Macklin

"Off my ship you!" he roared. "Every one of you; you're a gang of murdering cutthroats."

The deck-hands and the ship-stewards, who had gathered at the gangway to assist in throwing me down it, sprang to the Captain's aid.

"Over with him, boys," he roared. "Clear the ship of them. Throw them overboard." The crew fell upon the astonished soldiers, and drove them to the side. Their curses and shrieks filled the air, the women retreated screaming, and I was left alone, leaning limply against the cabin with my revolver hanging from my fingers.

It began and ended in an instant, and as the ship moved forward and the last red-breeched soldier disappeared headforemost down the companion-ladder, the Captain rushed back to me and clutched me by both shoulders. Had it not been for the genial grin on his fat face, I would have thought that he meant to hurl me after the others.

"Now then, Captain Macklin," he cried, "you come with me. You come to my cabin, and that's where you stay as long as you are on my ship. You're no passenger, you're my guest, and there's nothing on board too good for you."

"But I don't—understand," I protested faintly. "What does it mean?"

"What does it mean?" he shouted. "It means you're the right sort for me! I haven't heard of nothing but your goings-on for the last three trips. Vice-President of Honduras!" he exclaimed, shaking me as though I were a carpet. "A kid like you! You come to my cabin and tell me the whole yarn from start to finish. I'd rather carry you than old man Huntington himself!"

The passengers had returned, and stood listening to his exclamations, in a wondering circle. The stewards and deck-hands, panting with their late exertions, were grinning at me with unmistakable interest.

"Bring Captain Macklin's breakfast to my cabin, you," he shouted to them. "And, Mr. Owen," he continued, addressing the Purser, with great impressiveness, "this is Captain Macklin, himself. He's going with us as my guest."

With a wink, he cautiously removed my revolver from my fingers, and slapped me jovially on the shoulder. "Son!" he exclaimed, "I wouldn't have missed the sight of you holding your gun on that gang for a cargo of bullion. I suspicioned it was you, the moment you did it. That will be something for me to tell them in 'Frisco, that will. Now, you come along," he added, suddenly, with parental solicitude, "and take a cup of coffee, and a dose of quinine, or you'll be ailing."

He pushed a way for me through the crowd of passengers, who fell back in two long lines. As we moved between them, I heard a woman's voice ask, in a loud whisper:

" Who did you say? "

A man's voice answered, " Why, Captain Macklin," and then protested, in a rising accent, " Now, for Heaven's sake, Jennie, don't tell me you don't know who he is? "

That was my first taste of fame. It was a short-lived, limited sort of fame, but at that time it stretched throughout all Central America. I doubt if it is sufficiently robust to live in the cold latitudes of the North. It is just an exotic of the tropics. I am sure it will never weather Cape Hatteras. But although I won't amount to much in Dobbs Ferry, down here in Central America I am pretty well known, and during these last two months that I have been lying, very near to death, in the Canal Company's hospital, my poor little fame stuck by me, and turned strangers into kind and generous friends.

DOBBS FERRY, September, 1882

September passed before I was a convalescent, and it was the first of October when the Port of Sydney passed Sandy Hook, and I stood at the bow, trembling with cold and happiness, and saw the autumn leaves on the hills of Staten Island and the thousands of columns of circling, white smoke rising over the three cities. I had not let Beatrice and Aunt Mary know that I was in a hospital, but had told them that I was making my way home slowly, which was true enough, and that they need not expect to hear from me until I had arrived in New York City. So, there was no one at the dock to meet me.

But, as we came up the harbor, I waved at the people on the passing ferry-boats, and they, shivering, no doubt, at the sight of our canvas awnings and the stewards' white jackets, waved back, and gave me my first welcome home.

It was worth all the disappointments, and the weeks in hospital, to stick my head in the ticket-window of the Grand Central Station, and hear myself say, "Dobbs Ferry, please." I remember the fascination with which I watched the man (he was talking over his shoulder to another man at the time) punch the precious ticket, and toss it to me. I suppose in his life he has many times sold tickets to Dobbs Ferry, but he never sold them as often as I had rehearsed asking him for that one.

I had wired them not to meet me at the station, but to be waiting at the house, and when I came up the old walk, with the box-hedges on either side, they were at the door, and Aunt Mary ran to meet me, and hugged and scolded me, and cried on my shoulder, and Beatrice smiled at me, just as though she were very proud of me, and I kissed her once. After ten minutes, it did not seem as though I had ever been away from home. And, when I looked at Beatrice, and I could not keep my eyes from her, I was filled with wonder that I had ever had the courage to go from where she was. We were very happy.

I am afraid that for the next two weeks I traded upon their affection scandalously. But it was their own fault. It was their wish that I should constantly pose in the dual rôles of the returned prodigal and Othello, and, as I told them, if I were an obnoxious prig ever after, they alone were responsible.

I had the ravenous hunger of the fever-convalescent, and I had an audience that would have turned General Grant into a braggart. So, every day wonderful dishes of Aunt Mary's contriving were set before me, and Beatrice would not open a book so long as there was one adventure I had left untold.

And this, as I soon learned, was the more flattering, as she had already heard most of them at second-hand.

Captain Macklin

I can remember my bewilderment that first evening as I was relating the story of the duel, and she corrected me.

"Weren't you much nearer?" she asked. "You fired at twenty paces."

"So we did," I cried, "but how could you know that?"

"Mr. Lowell told us," she said.

"Lowell!" I shouted. "Has Lowell been here?"

"Yes, he brought us your sword," Beatrice answered. "Didn't you see where we placed it?" and she rose rather quickly, and stood with her face toward the fireplace, where, sure enough, my sword was hanging above the mantel.

"Oh yes," said Aunt Mary, "Mr. Lowell has been very kind. He has come out often to ask for news of you. He is at the Brooklyn Navy Yard. We like him so much," she added.

"Like him!" I echoed. "I should think you would! Isn't that bully," I cried, "to think of his being so near me, and that he's a friend of yours already. We must have him out to-morrow. Isn't he fine, Beatrice?"

She had taken down the sword, and was standing holding it out to me.

"Yes, he is," she said, "and he is very fond of you, too, Royal. I don't believe you've got a better friend."

Captain Macklin

Attractive as the prodigal son may seem at first, he soon becomes a nuisance. Even Othello when he began to tell over his stories for the second time must have been something of a bore. And when Aunt Mary gave me roast beef for dinner two nights in succession, and after dinner Beatrice picked up " Lorna Doone " and retired to a corner, I knew that I had had my day.

The next morning at breakfast, in a tone of gentle reproach, I announced that I was going out into the cold world, as represented by New York City, to look for a job. I had no idea of doing anything of the sort. I only threw out the suggestion tentatively, and I was exceedingly disgusted when they caught up my plan with such enthusiasm and alacrity, that I was forced to go on with it. I could not see why it was necessary for me to work. I had two thousand dollars a year my grandfather had left me, and my idea of seeking for a job, was to look for it leisurely, and with caution. But the family seemed to think that, before the winter set in, I should take any chance that offered, and, as they expressed it, settle down.

None of us had any very definite ideas as to what I ought to do, or even that there was anything I could do. Lowell, who is so much with us now, that I treat him like one of the family, argued that to business men my strongest recommendation would be my knowledge of languages. He said I ought to try for a clerkship in some firm where I could handle the foreign correspondence. His even suggesting such work annoyed me extremely. I told him that, on the contrary, my strongest card was my experience in active campaigning, backed by my thorough military education, and my ability to command men. He said unfeelingly, that you must first catch your men, and that in down-town business circles a military education counted for no more than a college-course in football.

"You good people don't seem to understand," I explained (we were holding a family council on my case at the time); "I have no desire to move in down-town business circles. I hate business circles."

"Well, you must live, Royal," Aunt Mary said. "You have not enough money to be a gentleman of leisure."

"Royal wouldn't be content without some kind of work," said Beatrice.

"No, he can't persuade us he's not ambitious!" Lowell added. "You mean to make something of yourself, you know you do, and you can't begin too early."

Since Lowell has been promoted to the ward-room, he talks just like a grandfather.

"Young man," I said, "I've seen the day when you were an ensign, and I was a Minister of War, and you had to click your heels if you came within thirty feet of my distinguished person. Of course, I'm ambitious, and the best proof of it is, that I don't want to sit in a bird-cage all my life, counting other people's money."

Aunt Mary looked troubled, and shook her head at me.

"Well, Royal," she remonstrated, "you've got very little of your own to count, and some day you'll want to marry, and then you'll be sorry."

I don't know why Aunt Mary's remark should have affected anyone except myself, but it seemed to take all the life out of the discussion, and Beatrice remembered she had some letters to write, and Lowell said he must go back to the Navy Yard, although when he arrived he told us he had fixed it with another man to stand his watch. The reason I was disturbed was because, when Aunt Mary spoke, it made me wonder if she were not thinking of Beatrice. One day just after I arrived from Panama, when we were alone, she said that while I was gone she had been in fear she might die before I came back, and that Beatrice would be left alone. I laughed at her and told her she would live a hundred years, and added, not meaning anything in particular, "And she'll not be alone. I'll be here."

Then Aunt Mary looked at me very sadly, and said: "Royal, I could die so contentedly if I thought you two were happy." She waited, as though she expected me to make some reply, but I couldn't think of anything to say, and so just looked solemn, then she changed the subject by asking: "Royal, have you noticed that Lieutenant Lowell admires Beatrice very much?" And I said, "Of course he does. If he didn't, I'd punch his head." At which she again looked at me in such a wistful, pained way, smiling so sadly, as though for some reason she were sorry for me.

They all seemed to agree that I had had my fling, and should, as they persisted in calling it, "settle down." A most odious phrase. They were two to one against me, and when one finished another took it up. So that at last I ceased arguing and allowed myself to be bullied into looking for a position.

But before surrendering myself to the downtown business circles I made one last effort to remain free.

In Honduras, Laguerre had told me that a letter to the Crédit Lyonnais in Paris would always find him. I knew that since his arrival at

San Francisco he had had plenty of time to reach Paris, and that if he were there now he must know whether there is anything in this talk of a French expedition against the Chinese in Tonkin. Also whether the Mahdi really means to make trouble for the Khedive in the Soudan. Laguerre was in the Egyptian army for three years, and knows Baker Pasha well. I was sure that if there was going to be trouble, either in China or Egypt, he could not keep out of it.

So I cabled him to the Crédit Lyonnais, " Are you well? If going any more campaigns, please take me." I waited three restless weeks for an answer, and then, as no answer came, I put it all behind me, and hung my old, torn uniform where I would not see it, and hid the presentation-sword behind the eight-day clock in the library.

Beatrice raised her eyes from her book and watched me.

" Why? " she asked.

" It hurts me," I said.

She put down her book, and for a long time looked at me without speaking.

" I did not know you disliked it as much as that," she said. " I wonder if we are wrong. And yet," she added, smiling, "it does not seem a great sacrifice; to have work to do, to live at home, and in such a dear, old home as this, near a big city, and with the river in front and the country all about you. It seems better than dying of wounds in a swamp, or of fever in a hospital."

"I haven't complained. I'm taking my medicine," I answered. "I know you all wouldn't ask it of me, if you didn't think it was for my good." I had seated myself in front of the wood fire opposite her, and was turning the chain she gave me round and round my wrist. I slipped it off, and showed it to her as it hung from my fingers, shining in the firelight.

"And yet," I said, "it was fine being your Knight-Errant, and taking risks for your sake, and having only this to keep me straight." I cannot see why saying just that should have disturbed her, but certainly my words, or the sight of the chain, had a most curious effect. It is absurd, but I could almost swear that she looked frightened. She flushed, and her eyes were suddenly filled with tears. I was greatly embarrassed. Why should she be afraid of me? I was too much upset to ask her what was wrong, so I went on hastily: "But now I'll have you always with me, to keep me straight," I said.

She laughed at that, a tremulous little laugh, and said: "And so you won't want it any more, will you?"

"Won't want it," I protested gallantly. "I'd like to see anyone make me give it up."

"You'd give it up to me, wouldn't you?" she asked gently. "It looks—" she added, and stopped.

"I see," I exclaimed. "Looks like a pose, sort of effeminate, a man's wearing a bracelet. Is that what you think?"

She laughed again, but this time quite differently. She seemed greatly relieved.

"Perhaps that's it," she said. "Give it me, Royal. You'll never need any woman's trinkets to keep you straight."

I weighed the gold links in the hollow of my palm.

"Do you really want it?" I asked. She raised her eyes eagerly. "If you don't mind," she said.

I dropped the chain into her hand, but as I turned toward the fire, I could not help a little sigh. She heard me, and leaned forward. I could just see her sweet, troubled face in the fire-light. "But I mean to return it you, Royal," she said, "some day, when—when you go out again to fight wind-mills."

"That's safe!" I returned, roughly. "You know that time will never come. The three of you together have fixed that. I'm no longer a knight-errant. I'm a business-man now. I'm not to remember I ever was a knight-errant. I must even give up my Order of the Golden Chain, because it's too romantic, because it might remind me that somewhere in this world there is romance, and adventure, and fighting. And it wouldn't do. You can't have romance around a business office. Some day, when I was trying to add up my sums, I might see it on my wrist, and forget where I was. I might remember the days when it shone in the light of a camp-fire, when I used to sleep on the ground with my arm under my head, and it was the last thing I saw, when it seemed like your fingers on my wrist holding me back, or urging me forward. Business circles would not allow that. They'd put up a sign, ' Canvassers, pedlers, and Romance not admitted.' "

The first time I applied for a job I was unsuccessful. The man I went to see had been an instructor at Harvard when my uncle was professor there, and Aunt Mary said he had been a great friend of Professor Endicott's. One day in the laboratory the man discovered something, and had it patented. It brought him a fortune, and he was now president of a company which manufactured it, and with branches all over the world.

Aunt Mary wrote him a personal letter about

me, in the hope that he might put me in charge of the foreign correspondence.

He kept me waiting outside his office-door for one full hour. During the first half-hour I was angry, but the second half-hour I enjoyed exceedingly. By that time the situation appealed to my sense of humor. When the great man finally said he would see me, I found him tilting back in a swivel-chair in front of a mahogany table. He picked out Aunt Mary's letter from a heap in front of him, and said: "Are you the Mr. Macklin mentioned in this letter? What can I do for you?"

I said very deliberately: "You can do nothing for me. I have waited one hour to tell you so. When my aunt, Mrs. Endicott, does anyone the honor to write him a letter, there is no other business in New York City more important than attending promptly to that letter. I *had* intended becoming a partner in your firm; now, I shall not. You are a rude, fat, and absurd, little person. Good-morning."

I crossed over to the Brooklyn Navy Yard, and told Lowell and the other watch-officers in the ward-room of my first attempt to obtain a job. They laughed until I hoped they would strangle.

"Who the devil do you think you are, anyway," they cried, "going around, insulting millionnaires like that?"

After leaving the cruiser that afternoon, I was so miserable that I could have jumped into the East River. It was the sight of the big, brown guns did it, and the cutlasses in their racks, and the clean-limbed, bare-throated Jackies, and the watch-officer stamping the deck just as though he were at sea, with his glass and side-arms. And when the marine at the gate of the yard shifted his gun and challenged me, it was so like old times that I could have fallen on his neck and hugged him.

Over the wharves, all along my way to the ferry, the names of strange and beautiful ports mocked at me from the sheds of the steam-ship lines; "Bahia, Rio de Janeiro, and the River Plata," "Guayaquil, Callao, and Santiago," "Cape Town, Durban, and Lorenzo Marquez." It was past six o'clock and very dark. The ice was pushing and grinding against the pier-heads, and through the falling snow the tall buildings in New York twinkled with thousands of electric lights, like great Christmas-trees. At one wharf a steamer of the Red D line, just in from La Guayra, was making fast, and I guiltily crept on board. Without, she was coated in a sheating of ice, but within she reeked of Spanish-America—

shopping," she added. "She's in there. I'm waiting for her." She seemed to think that the situation required a chaperon.

"You mustn't say they were my shells, Miss Fiske," I protested. "I may insult a woman for protecting her brother's life, but I never fire shells at her."

It did not surprise me to hear myself laughing at the words which, when she spoke them, had seemed so terrible. It was as though none of it had ever occurred. It was part of a romantic play, and we had seen the play together. Who could believe that the young man, tramping the streets on the lookout for a job, had ever signed his name, as vice-president of Honduras, to a passport for Joseph Fiske; that the beautiful girl in the sables, with her card-case in her hand, had ever heard the shriek of shrapnel?

And she exclaimed, just as though we had both been thinking aloud: "No, it's not possible, is it?"

"It never happened," I said.

"But I tell you what has happened," she went on, eagerly, "or perhaps you know. Have you heard what my father did?"

I said I had not. I refrained from adding that I believed her father capable of doing almost anything.

"Then I'm the first to tell you the news," she exclaimed. She nodded at me energetically. "Well, he's paid that money. He owed it all the time.'

"That's not news," I said.

She flushed a little, and laughed.

"But, indeed, father was not to blame," she exclaimed. "They deceived him dreadfully. But when we got home, he looked it up, and found you were right about that money, and so he's paid it back, not to that odious Alvarez man, but in some way, I don't quite understand how, but so the poor people will get it."

"Good!" I cried.

"And he's discharged all that Isthmian crowd," she went on.

"Better," I said.

"And made my brother president of the new company," she continued, and then raised her eyebrows, and waited, smiling.

"Oh, well," I said, "since he's your brother— 'best.'"

"That's right," she cried. "That's very nice of you. Here comes mother. I want you to meet her."

Mother came toward us, out of a French dress-maker's. It was one of the places I had decided against, when I had passed it a few minutes before. It seemed one of the few business houses where a French linguist would be superfluous.

I was presented as " Captain Macklin—who, you know, mother—who fought the duel with Arthur—that is, who didn't shoot at him."

Mrs. Fiske looked somewhat startled. Even to a trained social leader it must be trying to have a man presented to you on a sidewalk as the one who did not shoot your son.

Mrs. Fiske had a toy dog under one arm, and was holding up her train, but she slipped the dog to the groom, and gave me her hand.

" How do you do, Mr.—Captain Macklin," she said. " My son has told me a great deal about you. Have you asked Captain Macklin to come to see us, Helen?" she said, and stepped into the brougham.

" Come in any day after five," said Miss Fiske, " and we'll have tortillas and frijoles, and build a camp-fire in the library. What's your address?"

" Dobbs Ferry," I said.

" Just Dobbs Ferry?" she asked. " But you're such a well-known person, Captain Macklin."

" I'm Mr. Macklin now," I answered, and I tried to shut the door on them, but the groom seemed to think that was his privilege, and so I

bowed, and they drove away. Then I went at
once to a drug-store and borrowed the directory,
to find out where they lived, and I walked all the
way up the avenue to have a look at their house.
Somehow I felt that for that day I could not go
on asking for a job. I saw a picture of myself
on a high stool in the French dressmaker's writing to the Paris house for more sable cloaks for
Mrs. Fiske.

The Fiske mansion overlooks Central Park,
and it is as big as the Academy of Music. I
found that I knew it well by sight. I at once
made up my mind that I never would have the
courage to ring that door-bell, and I mounted a
Fifth Avenue stage, and took up my work of rec-
onnoitring for a job where Miss Fiske had interrupted it.

The next day I got the job. I am to begin
work on Monday. It is at Schwartz & Carboy's.
They manufacture locks and hinges and agricult-
ural things. I saw a lot of their machetes in
Honduras with their paper stamp on the blade.
They have almost a monopoly of the trade in
South America. Fortunately, or unfortunately,
one of their Spanish clerks had left them, and
when I said I had been in Central America and
could write Spanish easily, Schwartz, or, it may
have been Carboy—I didn't ask him which was

his silly name—dictated a letter and I wrote it in Spanish. One of the other clerks admitted it was faultless. So, I regret to say, I got the job. I'm to begin with fifteen dollars, and Schwartz or Carboy added, as though it were a sort of a perquisite: "If our young men act gentlemanly, and are good dressers, we often send them to take our South American customers to lunch. The house pays the expenses. And in the evenings you can show them around the town. Our young men find that an easy way of seeing the theatres for nothing."

Knowing the tastes of South Americans visiting New York, I replied severely that my connection with Schwartz & Carboy would end daily at four in the afternoon, but that a cross-town car passed Koster & Bial's every hour. I half hoped he would take offence at that, and in consequence my connection with Schwartz & Carboy might end instantly and forever; but whichever one he was, only laughed and said: "Yes, those Brazilians are a queer lot. We eat up most of our profits bailing them out of police courts the next morning. Well—you turn up Monday."

Captain Macklin

It's all over. It will be a long time before I add another chapter to my "Memoirs." When I have written this one they are to be sealed, and to-morrow they are to be packed away in Aunt Mary's cedar chest. I am now writing these lines after everyone else has gone to bed.

It happened after dinner. Aunt Mary was upstairs, and Beatrice was at the piano. We were waiting for Lowell, who had promised to come up and spend the evening. I was sitting at the centre-table, pretending to read, but watching Beatrice. Her back was turned toward me, so I could stare at her as long as I pleased. The light of the candles on each side of the music-rack fell upon her hair, and made it flash and burn. She had twisted it high, in a coil, and there never was anything more lovely than the burnished copper against the white glow of her skin, nor anything so noble as the way her head rose upon her neck and sloping shoulders. It was like a flower on a white stem.

She was not looking at the music before her, but up at nothing, while her hands ran over the keyboard, playing an old sailor's "chantey" which Lowell has taught us. It carries with it all the sweep and murmur of the sea at night.

319

She could not see me, she had forgotten that I was even in the room, and I was at liberty to gaze at her and dream of her undisturbed. I felt that, without that slight, white figure always at my side, the life I was to begin on the morrow, or any other life, would be intolerable. Without the thought of Beatrice to carry me through the day I could not bear it. Except for her, what promise was there before me of reward or honor? I was no longer "an officer and a gentleman," I was a copying clerk, "a model letter-writer." I could foresee the end. I would become a nervous, knowing, smug-faced civilian. Instead of clean liquors, I would poison myself with cocktails and "quick-order" luncheons. I would carry a commuter's ticket. In time I might rise to the importance of calling the local conductors by their familiar names. "Bill, what was the matter with the 8.13 this morning?" From to-morrow forward I would be "our" Mr. Macklin, "Yours of even date received. Our Mr. Macklin will submit samples of goods desired." "Mr." Macklin! "Our" Mr. Macklin! Ye Gods! Schwartz & Carboy's Mr. Macklin!

I set my teeth and fixed my eyes on Beatrice. For her sake, but only for her sake could it be endured. If she could ever care for me, as I longed and hoped she might, I would submit to any servitude, I would struggle to rise above the most hateful surroundings.

I had just registered this mental vow, my eyes were still fixed appealingly on the woman who was all unconscious of the sacrifice I was about to make for her, when the servant came into the room and handed me a telegram. I signed for it, and she went out. Beatrice had not heard her enter, and was still playing. I guessed the telegram was from Lowell to say he could not get away, and I was sorry. But as I tore open the envelope, I noticed that it was not the usual one of yellow paper, but of a pinkish white. I had never received a cablegram. I did not know that this was one. I read the message, and as I read it the blood in every part of my body came to a sudden stop. There was a strange buzzing in my ears, the drums seemed to have burst with a tiny report. The shock was so tremendous that it seemed Beatrice must have felt it too, and I looked up at her stupidly. She was still playing.

The cablegram had been sent that morning from Marseilles. The message read, " Commanding Battalion French Zouaves, Tonkin Expedition, holding position of Adjutant open for you, rank of Captain, if accept join Marseilles. Laguerre."

I laid the paper on my knee, and sat staring, scarcely breathing, as though I were afraid if I moved I would wake. I was trembling and cold, for I was at the parting of the ways, and I knew it. Beyond the light of the candles, beyond the dull red curtains jealously drawn against the winter landscape, beyond even the slight, white figure with its crown of burnished copper, I saw the swarming harbor of Marseilles. I saw the swaggering turcos in their scarlet breeches, the crowded troop-ships, and from every ship's mast the glorious tri-color of France; the flag that in ten short years had again risen, that was flying over advancing columns in China, in Africa, in Madagascar; over armies that for Alsace Lorraine were giving France new and great colonies on every seaboard of the world. The thoughts that flew through my brain made my fingers clench until the nails bit into my palms. Even to dream of such happiness was actual pain. That this might come to me! To serve under the tri-color, to be a captain of the Grand Armée, to be one of the army reared and trained by Napoleon Bonaparte.

I heard a cheery voice, and Lowell passed me, and advanced bowing toward Beatrice, and she turned and smiled at him. But as she rose, she saw my face.

" Roy!" she cried. " What is it? What has happened ? "

I watched her coming toward me, as someone

projected from another life, a wonderful, beautiful memory, from a life already far in the past. I handed her the cablegram and stood up stiffly. My joints were rigid and the blood was still cold in my veins. She read the message, and gave a little cry, and stood silent, gazing at me. I motioned her to give it to Lowell, who was looking at us anxiously, his eyes filled with concern.

He kept his head lowered over the message for so long, that I thought he was reading it several times. When he again raised his face it was filled with surprise and disapproval. But beneath, I saw a dawning look which he could not keep down, of a great hope. It was as though he had been condemned to death, and the paper Beatrice had handed him to read had been his own reprieve.

"Tell me," said Beatrice. Her tone was as gentle and as solemn as the stroke of a bell, and as impersonal. It neither commended nor reproved. I saw that instantly she had determined to conceal her own wishes, to obliterate herself entirely, to let me know that, so far as she could affect my choice, I was a free agent. I looked appealingly from her to Lowell, and from Lowell back to Beatrice. I still was trembling with the fever the message had lit in me. When I tried to answer, my voice was hoarse and shaking.

" It's like drink!" I said.

Lowell raised his eyes as though he meant to speak, and then lowered them and stepped back, leaving Beatrice and myself together.

" I only want you to see," Beatrice began bravely, " how—how serious it is. Every one of us in his life must have a moment like this, and, if he could only know that the moment had come, he might decide wisely. You know the moment has come. You must see that this is the crisis. It means choosing not for a year, but for always." She held out her hands, entwining the fingers closely. " Oh, don't think I'm trying to stop you, Royal," she cried. " I only want you to see that it's final. I know that it's like strong drink to you, but the more you give way to it—. Don't you think, if you gave your life here a fairer trial, if you bore with it a little longer——"

She stopped sharply as though she recognized that, in urging me to a choice, she was acting as she had determined she would not. I did not answer, but stood in silence with my head bent, for I could not look at her. I knew now how much dearer to me, even than her voice, was the one which gave the call to arms. I did indeed understand that the crisis had come. In that same room, five minutes before the message arrived, I had sworn for her sake alone to submit to the life I hated.

And yet in an instant, without a moment's pause, at the first sound of " Boots and Saddles," I had sprung to my first love, and had forgotten Beatrice and my sworn allegiance. Knowing how greatly I loved her, I now could understand, since it made me turn from her, how much greater must be my love for this, her only rival, the old life that was again inviting me.

I was no longer to be deceived; the one and only thing I really loved, the one thing I understood and craved, was the free, homeless, untrammelled life of the soldier of fortune. I wanted to see the shells splash up the earth again, I wanted to throw my leg across a saddle, I wanted to sleep on a blanket by a camp-fire, I wanted the kiss and caress of danger, the joy which comes when the sword wins honor and victory together, and I wanted the clear, clean view of right and wrong, that is given only to those who hourly walk with death.

I raised my head, and spoke very softly:

" It is too late. I am sorry. But I have decided. I must go."

Lowell stepped out of the shadow, and faced me with the same strange look, partly of wonder, and partly of indignation.

" Nonsense, Royal," he said, " let *me* talk to you. We've been shipmates, or comrades, and all that sort of thing, and you've got to listen to me. Think, man, think what you're losing. Think of all the things you are giving up. Don't be a weak child. This will affect your whole life. You have no right to decide it in a minute."

I stepped to its hiding-place, and took out the sword my grandfather had carried in the Civil War; the sword I had worn in Honduras. I had hidden it away, that it might not remind me that once I, too, was a soldier. It acted on me like a potion. The instant my fingers touched its hilt, the blood, which had grown chilled, leaped through my body. In answer I held the sword toward Lowell. It was very hard to speak. They did not know how hard. They did not know how cruelly it hurt me to differ from them, and to part from them. The very thought of it turned me sick and miserable. But it was written. It had to be.

"You ask me to think of what I am giving up," I said, gently. "I gave up this. I shall never surrender it again. I am not deciding in a minute. It was decided for me long ago. It's a tradition. It's handed down to me. My grandfather was Hamilton, of Cerro Gordo, of the City of Mexico, of Gettysburg. My father was 'Fighting' Macklin. He was killed at the head of his soldiers. All my people have been soldiers. One fought at the battle of Princeton, one died fighting the king at Culloden. It's bred in me. It's in the blood. It's the blood of the Macklins that has decided this. And I—I am the last of the Macklins, and I must live and die like one."

The house is quiet now. They have all left me to my packing, and are asleep. Lowell went early and bade me good-by at the gate. He was very sad and solemn. "God bless you, Royal," he said, "and keep you safe, and bring you back to us." And I watched him swinging down the silent, moon-lit road, knocking the icicles from the hedges with his stick. I stood there some time looking after him, for I love him very dearly, and then a strange thing happened. After he had walked quite a distance from the house, he suddenly raised his head and began to whistle a jolly, rollicking sea-song. I could hear him for some minutes. I was glad to think he took it so light-heartedly. It is good to know that he is not jealous of my great fortune.

To-night we spared each other the parting words. But to-morrow they must be spoken, when Aunt Mary and Beatrice come to see me sail away on the French liner. The ship leaves at noon, and ten days later I shall be in Havre. Ye gods, to think that in ten days I shall see Paris! And then, the Mediterranean, the Suez Canal, the Indian Ocean, Singapore, and, at last, the yellow flags and black dragons of the enemy. It cannot last long, this row. I shall be coming home again in six months, unless the Mahdi makes trouble. Laguerre was three years in the Khedive's service, and with his influence an ex-captain of the French army should have little difficulty in getting a commission in Egypt.

Then, after that, I really will come home. But not as an ex-soldier. This time I shall come home on furlough. I shall come home a real officer, and play the prodigal again to the two noblest and sweetest and best women in God's world. All women are good, but they are the best. All women are so good, that when one of them thinks one of us is worthy to marry her, she pays a compliment to our entire sex. But as they are all good and all beautiful, Beatrice being the best and most beautiful, I was right not to think of marrying only one of them. With the world full of good women, and with a fight always going on somewhere, I am very wise not to "settle down." I know I shall be very happy.

In a year I certainly must come back, a foreign officer on leave, and I shall go to West Point and pay my respects to the Commandant. The men who saw me turned out will have to present arms to me, and the older men will say to the plebs, " That distinguished-looking officer with the French mustache, and the red ribbon of the Legion of Honor, is Captain Macklin. He was turned out of here. Now he's only a soldier of fortune. He belongs to no country."

But when the battalion is drawn up at retreat and the shadows stretch across the grass, I shall take up my stand once more on the old parade ground, with all the future Grants and Lees around me, and when the flag comes down, I shall raise my hand with theirs, and show them that I have a country, too, and that the flag we salute together is my flag still.

THE END